"Alan, you *did* come in that window."

"Grown men do not come in windows."

"You know," Carroll said slowly, "that was probably the most romantic dream I've ever had...a dark stranger suddenly appearing at my window on a black night."

Alan walked to the door. "I swear, Caro, you have a vivid imagination."

"Yes."

"Furthermore, you should have storms put on those windows."

"Yes."

"A burglar could reach you by climbing that tree."

"Yes."

"And as for a nice, demure woman having dreams like that..." He shook his head in despair. "You've shocked me. Seriously shocked me."

"Sorry," she said gravely. "Better wipe that grin off your face, Alan."

Jeanne Grant

Jeanne Grant is a native of Michigan. Married with two children, she and her husband raise cherries and peaches on a farm near Lake Michigan. A graduate of Michigan State University, she worked as a counselor, teacher, and personnel manager before devoting her time to writing. She sold her first book to SECOND CHANCE AT LOVE on December 8, 1981. "I remember the date well because the next day was my birthday," she says, "and I was afraid to answer the phone for fear they'd changed their minds."

Writing involves her whole family. "The kids would probably be shocked if they had dinner on time, but they're more than willing to help me do research . . . from making chocolate, to mining silver, to exploring the ghost towns of northern Idaho."

Last year Jeanne won the Romance Writers of America Silver Medallion Award and the Romantic Times Award for sensual writing.

Dear Reader:

What could be lovelier than a day in June? The next six SECOND CHANCE AT LOVE romances, of course! Jeanne Grant sets the tone by indirectly asking: Have you ever sympathized with the "other man" in romances? The guy who's nice, but ... well, he's just not the hero. Does he ever find the woman of his dreams? In *No More Mr. Nice Guy* (#340), Jeanne Grant shouts a resounding "Yes!" You see, Alan Smith is a wonderful guy, and Carroll's deeply in love with him. But sometimes she wishes he were just a little less ... well, less predictable, cautious, and controlled! And when Alan sets out to be dashing, macho, and reckless—watch out! With humor and insight, Jeanne once again creates a hero and heroine you'll simply adore ... and a one-of-a-kind love story that you'll savor and remember...

Next, Katherine Granger shows her admirable versatility in *A Place in the Sun* (#341), in which brooding, embittered Rush Mason is hired as groundskeeper by Libby Peterson, the ladylike owner of a Cape Cod inn. As Rush's powerful presence seems to shrink the lush acreage of Libby's seaside estate, their heated glances lead to sultry, sexually charged encounters that will make your own skin prickle! Slowly the tension builds ... the mystery about Rush deepens. Here's steamy reading for a warm, melting June afternoon.

What woman hasn't dreamed of meeting a dashingly handsome, thoroughly princely man who will sweep her off her feet and take her "away from all this"? In Sherryl Woods's latest romance, *A Prince Among Men* (#342), this secret desire is fulfilled for actress-mime Erin Matthews ... and the wisdom of "Be careful what you wish for because it might come true" takes on a whole new meaning! Mysterious Mark Townsend's majestic courtship of Erin will tickle your funny bone and tug on your heartstrings.

In an inspired move, Jan Mathews unites erotic dancer Cindy Marshall from her previous romance *Slightly Scandalous* (#226) and vice-squad cop Brad Jordan from *Shady Lady* (#306) to bring you another sassy, sexy romance—*Naughty and Nice* (#343). Though Cindy's now a respectable social worker, she can't forget that she once stripped for a living—and she *won't* get involved with a man as unsuitable as Brad Jordan! Easier said than done—because Brad storms all her defenses ... and in record time! No one creates tough guys like Jan Mathews ... and no one else could have written a romance as wacky and wonderful as *Naughty and Nice*.

Next, Linda Raye returns after a long hiatus with *All the Right Moves* (#344), in which two strong-willed characters find themselves on opposite sides of an issue ... and in constant disagreement over their romantic future! Basketball coach Ryan McFadden, who simply oozes sexuality, knows at once that referee Lauren Nickels is the woman for him. But Lauren's determined to remain aloof—no matter how roguish his charm or penetrating his insight! Still, Ryan sees that beneath her tough exterior there lies a woman's secret longing. With such great ingredients for romance, it's only a matter of executing all the right moves before love triumphs.

Kelly Adams has a special talent for capturing the spirit of America's heartland—both the richness of the land and the simple honesty of the people. In *Blue Skies, Golden Dreams* (#345), city slicker Sara Scott arrives on Joe Dancy's Iowa farm intending to rescue her sister from what she considers his con-artist clutches. But with lighthearted teasing, indomitable integrity, and stubborn persistence, Joe sets Sara to baking cookies and going fishing ... turning her into a country girl and stampeding her emotions in one fell swoop! In Joe's conquest of Sara, Kelly Adams conveys a breath-catching tenderness and a reaffirmation of good living that makes your heart sing.

Have a terrific June, everyone! Warm wishes,

Ellen Edwards

Ellen Edwards, Senior Editor
SECOND CHANCE AT LOVE
The Berkley Publishing Group
200 Madison Avenue
New York, NY 10016

SECOND CHANCE AT LOVE™

JEANNE GRANT
NO MORE MR. NICE GUY

A™
SECOND CHANCE AT LOVE
BOOK

Second Chance at Love books are published by
The Berkley Publishing Group
200 Madison Avenue, New York, NY 10016

NO MORE MR. NICE GUY

Chapter 1

"WHOOPS!" IF SHE hadn't been precariously balancing a tray of champagne glasses, Carroll would have been happy to disappear from the kitchen again. As it was, she set the tray hastily on the counter with a rattling plunk. "I swear there isn't a room in the house safe from the two of you!"

Stéphane, her sister's new fiancé, removed his hands from Nancy long enough to offer a bold grin. Nancy just chuckled. "I can't control him," she confessed.

That Carroll already knew. Certainly a houseful of people hadn't inhibited Stéphane's amorous behavior where her sister was concerned.

It didn't matter. All that mattered to Carroll was that beneath the sophisticated trappings of red silk and a frothy hairstyle, Nancy was glowing.

Nancy was also leaving, with a not very subtle wink at Stéphane. "This is probably the only chance my two favorite people are going to have to get to know each other in this madhouse," she said deliberately. Seconds later, the door to the dining room was swinging shut behind her.

Silence swept through the kitchen on the backswing. Carroll covered it by immediately and noisily filling her mother's sink with sudsy water. Normally

1

comfortable with people, she was finding it strangely difficult to feel at ease with her future brother-in-law.

Twenty-four hours ago, Nancy had simply flown in from Quebec with Stéphane in tow. In itself, that wasn't surprising. Nance did everything whirlwind fashion, a characteristic she'd inherited from their mother. And while the two other Laker women panicked, Carroll had spent the afternoon between the store, telephone, and kitchen, organizing the impromptu engagement party that was now in full swing. Nothing to it, really. Carroll had always been the practical one in the family.

Being practical suited her. Being itchy-restless and irritable as she'd been all this evening certainly didn't, but banishing the odd mood was somehow harder with Stéphane standing there.

The small city of Lafayette, Indiana, didn't raise men like Stéphane, she thought. Men who looked as if they'd been born in tuxedos. Men with deliciously wild eyes. Men who exuded virility with the simple act of breathing. Men with slight French accents and a way of looking at a woman . . . well. Carroll held up a glass to inspect it for water spots. Hell's bells. How was she supposed to hold a conversation with a man like that? "You're surviving meeting every Laker relative from here to Poughkeepsie?" she asked lightly.

"Not Aunt Harriet."

"No one survives Aunt Harriet," she assured him.

"Then, too, my Nance does have her share of third cousins," Stéphane added dryly, tipping a glass of champagne to his lips. "On the other hand, you and your parents are the only ones who are really important to her."

"You're not worried, are you? You won over Mom and Dad in thirty seconds flat."

"Worried about your parents—no." Stéphane's midnight-blue eyes slid over her with the skill of a man who knew women. Lots of women. Carroll felt her cream-colored angora sweater and gray slacks promptly stripped and a naked twenty-seven-year-old speech therapist revealed, right down to the dimple on her fanny. "But I think you've reserved judgment about me so far, haven't you, Carroll?"

His perception embarrassed her. She'd never meant to let on that he made her feel uncomfortable. "I hardly know you."

"We met hours ago," he reminded her. "Long enough to form a first impression."

Carroll dipped her hand in the water, but there wasn't a single glass left to be washed. She reached for the dish towel, not looking at him. "You brought my sister home dripping with diamonds . . ."

"Which didn't impress you in the slightest."

"No," she admitted, and flashed him a smile. "I've never been much good at warming up to strangers, but I guarantee that if you make Nance happy, I'll drown you in so much love and approval that you won't know what hit you."

Stéphane laughed, throwing back his head. "I like you, Carroll—and I have every intention of making your sister happy. Truce?"

She hadn't been aware there was a war. She also hadn't been aware that he'd had any intention of suddenly leaning closer. His mouth touched hers; she tasted the dangerous flavor of an experienced kiss thief, caught the whiff of sandalwood and musk.

When he straightened, his palm lingered a second on her chin. "Your sister's going to give me nothing but trouble, you know. You're the kind of woman I always wanted to fall in love with, but there you have it. She's the one—was, is, and will be. You can trust me, Carroll."

Wonderful, she thought dizzily.

Seconds later, Stéphane left the kitchen. She knew darn well he'd meant nothing by the kiss. He'd already kissed half the women at the party. Some men were all dark hair, dark eyes, charm, and trouble. Nance could handle him. Carroll shuddered at the thought of even trying. Still . . .

Guilt was wanting your toes to tingle when a strange man kissed you. Particularly when you intended to marry another man.

She looked down at her hands, the same hands that seemed intent on drying and redrying themselves on the kitchen towel. Tossing the towel aside, she took a breath, and desperately wanted Alan.

But instead of searching him out, she ducked into the bathroom down the hall, whisked a lipstick from her purse, and bent toward the vanity mirror to apply it. Her reflection showed a frowning woman. It was an average sort of frown.

And the average frown was backed up by a half-dozen other average features . . . Spaniel-brown eyes, an oval face with delicately arched brows, spiked bangs, and a short, windswept hair style. Her hair color was sort of blond and sort of brown, almost streaky looking but nothing really striking. Decent figure, nothing special. To give herself credit, she had terrific skin . . . if a man waxed poetic over complexions. Carroll had never had a man wax poetic over anything about her, and would have been annoyed if one had.

She'd always liked her looks just fine. Anyway, mature adult women didn't want glib flattery. Mature adult women didn't want an Adonis who attracted other women like moths to a flame and took effusive public displays of affection for granted. They wanted a man they could count on through thick and thin. Carroll was a mature adult woman. Objectively, she had no interest in a relationship with a man like Stéphane.

Unobjectively, and probably as a result of two glasses of champagne, she wished she could be less sensible for about thirty short minutes. No longer than that. She'd just like to be kidnapped by a swash-buckling, womanizing, sexy hero-type for one quick fling before she settled down for good. The thought, of course, was idiotic, and promoted more guilt. Alan was absolutely everything she could want in a mate. Everything. It was just . . .

A rap on the door made her chin jerk up. Nancy's head popped in. Within seconds, her sister had perched on the edge of the porcelain tub just as she'd done a thousand times when they were growing up. There were three bathrooms in the house, but this was the one where they'd discussed the truly critical issues in life, like boys, grades, first bras, and where babies came from.

In scarlet silk and spike heels, Nancy looked more polished these days, but her pretty features could still hold that so-young vulnerability when they were alone together. "Well? Did you two have a second to talk? You do like him, don't you, Carroll?"

Carroll dropped the lipstick into her purse and took a good look at Nancy's deliriously happy smile. "Of course I like him," she reassured.

Nancy sighed. "He's wildly romantic. And impulsive. And heaven knows, he's attractive to other women. He won't be the easiest man to hold . . ."

"You'll manage." If anyone could hold the devil who'd kissed her in the kitchen, Carroll laid odds on her sister.

"Did I show you the earrings he gave me?"

Only about forty times, but Carroll obediently bent to study the full-carat rocks in her sister's earlobes. "Gorgeous."

"I couldn't say no to him the first time I met him. That's just it, Caro. Even after all this time, it's still the same when he touches me," Nancy confessed. The dreamy look on her face gradually drifted away. Her lightly penciled brows arched in a scolding frown. "And you didn't say a word in your letters about your Alan! Here you're practically at the altar yourself."

"He hasn't asked me," Carroll said hastily.

"He will. Caro, he seems like a wonderful man. I've been worried about you for so long . . ."

"Me?" Carroll said with surprise. No one ever worried about her. No one needed to, and that was how she liked it.

"*You,*" her sister affirmed, and then grinned. "I certainly hope you're sleeping with him. And don't give me that look. For years you've needed a little good solid sin in your life."

"On a level with one-a-day vitamins?"

"Don't joke. You've always needed a man to whisk the caution right out from under you. Make you take down your hair . . ."

"That would be tough. I'm wearing it short."

". . . sweep you right off your feet . . ."

"Sounds like a bruise on the rear end to me."

Nancy stood up in a swirl of silk and Shalimar. "So you're not sleeping with him yet," she said sagely, in that patronizing tone of voice Carroll had nearly killed her for several times when they were teenagers. "Funny. I took one look at your Alan and figured him for a smart man."

"He is an *extremely* intelligent man."

"A sweetheart. I loved him on sight," Nancy affirmed. "I just figured he had more sense."

"We've only been seriously dating for the last couple of months," Carroll said irritably.

"And you've got him terrified into believing you have to be treated c-a-r-e-f-u-l-l-y. You've been doing that to men ever since I can remember."

"What on earth are you talking about? Is there something wrong with getting to know someone before you jump into bed with him?"

"Nope." Nancy flashed her mischievous smile and opened the door. "Only you've never held out on a man because of principles, Caro. In fact, I'll bet your fantasies are a thousand times wilder than mine. You just always intimidated the boys by being so *good*, I think you've got yourself fooled. Want me to explain all this to Alan?"

"If you want your funeral to precede your wedding."

"I was just going to tell him that it's all right to

take off your halo," Nancy said in an injured tone.

Carroll shook her head, suddenly laughing. "Two years in a big city didn't change you, thank heavens."

"Was it supposed to?"

"No."

Laughing, arms around each other, the sisters joined the party. The Lakers' blue and white living room smelled of smoke, champagne, and various perfumes. David Laker owned an insurance agency; Maud taught drama at Purdue. Between David, Maud, and their daughters, the family knew nearly everyone in Lafayette—and the whole town seemed to have turned out for the party.

The mood from room to room was magical. Anyone with a lick of sense could look at Nancy and Stéphane and guess the marriage would have its share of problems. No one cared. Everyone loves a lover, Carroll thought absently. Wandering through the crowded living room, she paused for the dozenth time to watch Stéphane and Nancy together.

He looked at Nancy as if she were forbidden fruit. Nance's face was flushed, as if every stolen kiss were dangerous and delicious. And every time Carroll looked at them, she could feel that annoyingly restless mood steal up on her again.

She knew what she wanted from her life. She was sure of herself, her values, her feelings. Just once, though, it would be nice to be that wanted, by any man. To be that foolish, that crazy in love, that silly with it, that wildly, dramatically, giddily oblivious to the whole damn world.

Where was Alan?

She finally tracked him down in the den, trapped in a conversational circle with several young mothers —not surprisingly. Alan Smith was a pediatrician, and at every gathering they'd ever been to he was plucked for free advice.

One look at him and she told herself she felt safe again. Alan was the kind of man whom a stranger instinctively trusted. He was also the kind of man who reached back and enclosed her hand in his when he couldn't possibly have seen her come up behind him. Security was the hello-again of his five fingers laced between hers.

The patter was all about measles symptoms, then whether aspirin was more effective than non-aspirin pain relievers. She'd heard the conversation before, which allowed her a moment to study Alan seriously as she hadn't studied him in a long time.

He wasn't a Stéphane. He wasn't a wildly romantic adventurer; he wasn't a man who spoke French and knew women far too well; he wasn't . . . a hero.

Alan was just a man. A good man, and it showed in everything about him. His voice was deep and quiet, with the soothing quality of heated brandy on an icy day. He wasn't overly tall; his Brooks Brothers suit was inevitably gray, and his conservative tie was inevitably just a little askew. Warm brown hair framed clean-cut, square features. He moved quietly, like the man he was, and his dark blue eyes always seemed to hold a smile. At thirty-three, he already had a network of fine lines around his eyes, character lines that reflected the compassion, intelligence, and patience that were so much a part of him.

Heaven knew Alan had been patient with her.

They'd known each other for six months and had been seriously dating for two. No man waited that long without pressing to sleep with a woman. Why should he? Any female in her right mind would have said yes long before this.

And Carroll had wanted to say yes, except that these last two months, when he gently steered the conservation toward houses and children, she knew that an invitation to bed was an invitation to marriage as well. Alan wasn't the type to play games. He was the type to love and be loved, and Carroll did love him. She'd never wanted a wild seducer with wicked eyes; she'd never wanted a Stéphane. She wanted the warmth of a fire, not the burn of it.

So why on earth was she still holding back from him?

Alan turned, finally able to separate himself from the others. He flashed her a smile that was uniquely Alan, warm and reassuring. She smiled back, yet that strange panic suddenly assaulted her full force. The "something" was wrong with her, not Alan; she knew that. But knowing that didn't make it go away. As if a black cat had darted in front of her, she had the sudden urge to hold on tighter, to hurry-hurry them both away from the crowd before something terrible could happen.

She did no such thing, of course. "I didn't mean to desert you for so long," she said lightly. "My sister sidetracked me and—"

"Of course she did. You two haven't seen each other in months. I expected that."

And understood. Alan always understood. Understanding was such a rare quality in a man, but just once Carroll wished he were slightly less understanding and more inclined to steal her off to a corner and kiss her senseless.

Actually, she would have killed him if he'd done any such thing.

Really, it would be tremendously helpful if someone would simply pour a bucket of cold water over her head before this ridiculous mood went too far.

"Carroll?"

She lifted her head and smiled, forcing herself to remember the thread of conversation. "Nancy definitely dropped a bomb on the family when she came home with Stéphane, engaged, no less. And to put a wedding together in less than a month . . ."

"Why do I get the feeling that your sister has always had a habit of starting earthquakes?"

"Tidal waves on occasion," Carroll admitted. "That's just Nance. We're nothing alike. She's always been the wildly exciting one in the family." Her glance wandered to her sister as Nancy walked into the room, her red lips tilted up to her fiancé in laughter. "She's beautiful, isn't she, Alan?"

"Hmm?"

"Don't you think so?" Carroll's eyes jumped back to his, but Alan wasn't looking at her sister. He was staring down at her.

"You're the beauty, Caro, don't you know that?" he said quietly.

She laughed, embarrassed by the compliment. "I'm not jealous of my sister," she assured him. "I'm proud of her. She has such courage; she's so full of life, so vibrant . . ."

Her mother interrupted them. Outside it had

started pouring, and people were beginning to leave; Maud was in a tizzy, unable to find a single spare umbrella. Carroll found them, and after that she could hardly desert her mother with the party mess to handle alone. It was an hour later when Alan brought her coat and they went in search of Stéphane and Nancy to say a last good night.

They discovered the engaged couple wrapped together in the hall just off the kitchen. Carroll exchanged an amused glance with Alan, but that odd feeling was there again. Standing next to Stéphane and Nancy was like intruding on the radiance of fire. They shot sparks off each other that could light up a sky. Alan's gentle hand on her shoulder suddenly felt as exciting as flannel pajamas.

Which was an unfair, shallow comparison, cruel to Alan and completely unlike herself. *Carroll, can't you stop this? Please stop this . . .*

But the nagging unease refused to disappear. Maybe Carroll had never wanted a roller coaster, but she was suddenly afraid to have missed the ride. In her heart and head, she didn't want an impatient and demanding lover, she wanted the gentleness and compassion she knew she would find with Alan. Still . . . just once in her life, just *once,* she would like to feel reckless and uninhibited and wanton, to know what it was like to feel wildly, crazily, insanely in love.

By one in the morning, the rain had stopped. Shivering, Carroll climbed into Alan's car and huddled until he came around to the other side and started the engine. Leaves were still clinging to the trees in mid-October, all shades of rust and crimson by day. By night, the leaves glistened black and silver, and a total stillness pervaded the quiet neighborhood. Alan's sedate New Yorker purred the few miles to her apartment.

"You're awfully quiet," Alan commented.

"Just tired." Carroll slipped off her shoes and curled her legs under her for warmth until the heater started working. It was exactly the kind of thing she could do so naturally with Alan, one of the tiny things that made up loving him. Real love, not idiotic fantasies.

"Sure that's all?" Alan asked. "You look troubled about something. Your sister?"

"There's nothing, really. Just a long day. Nance could always burn the candle at both ends, but I'm afraid I'm doomed to be the yawn-at-ten type." Her sleepy tone was wry, yet somehow lacked her usual easy humor. From the beginning of the relationship, she'd been totally honest about herself with Alan. People could get hurt if they had mistaken illusions about what they wanted and needed in a lover. Only tonight, just tonight, the honesty she'd built with him yawned in front of her like an abyss.

Alan, what if you're feeling cheated? Truly sexy lovers don't yawn at ten. They also don't curl up on car seats like kittens. A truly sexy lover would probably be half on your lap as you drove, prepared to strip for your private show before lovemaking . . .

Even the thought was enough to bring an embarrassed flush to her cheeks. Alan would probably commit her to an asylum if she tried nonsense like that.

"Something," he said firmly, "is on your mind. You don't care for your brother-in-law-to-be?"

"Did *you* like Stéphane?" she countered.

Alan answered thoughtfully, "Well enough. He's obviously intelligent, successful at what he does, sure of what he wants. I suppose I respect any man who marches to the beat of his own drummer."

Carroll turned her head. "Maybe he marches a bit too fast? Alan, do you think he'll be faithful to my sister?"

Alan's eyebrows shot up in surprise at the question. "Is that what you've been worried about? That he won't make her happy?"

"He's a good-looking man. Maybe too good-looking. Used to a lot of bright lights and glitter, traveling around the world . . ."

"Your sister isn't exactly a stay-at-home type herself."

"No," Carroll agreed absently. Nancy liked excitement, and if there wasn't any readily available, she was good at creating it. So unlike Carroll, who had always found excitement in a fire on a snowy evening, who got high on a simple breeze on a spring day, who felt utter exhilaration in a storm. Carroll made no apologies about who she was, but comparing herself to her sister was like comparing violets to orchids.

Alan pulled into the parking lot of her apartment house, and turned off the engine. "Still thinking about the two of them?"

"No, not really." She sighed. "Pay no attention to me, would you? I seem to be in the silliest mood. Believe me, it'll go away with a good night's sleep."

She stepped out of the car, and shivered. The black streets still shone wetly from the rain, and the night had turned bitter. Alan lifted an arm and tucked her into the warmth of his shoulder. Held close, she felt her restlessness almost disappear. Being held by Alan, touched by Alan, was to be cocooned in safety and warmth, safe from all the bitter winds.

When he paused at the front door, she lifted her face for the kiss she knew was coming. His lips came down gently on hers, wooing, cajoling. His taste was familiar by now. Alan's kisses were good; they were always good. His smooth-shaven cheek, the shape of his mouth, the softest swirl of his tongue inside her parted lips . . . she loved being kissed by Alan.

When he raised his head, his eyes shone down on her like stars on a midnight lake. She saw the question in them. It wasn't a question for tonight; it was late and both faced a normal busy workday in the morning. Still, the faintest trace of impatience was there on her features. He'd made it increasingly clear he wanted to spend his life with her. How long was she going to make him wait before inviting an intimate relationship between them?

She didn't know. She didn't know, couldn't think, and was tired of trying. Instead of pulling back as he undoubtedly expected, she laid her cheek on his shoulder and nuzzled closer for just a minute more, needing something she couldn't name.

"Caro?" His fingers sifted soothingly in her hair.

His warm breath fanned her temples.

"I love you," she said fiercely. "Kiss me, Alan. Please. Just . . ."

"Sweetheart, tell me what's wrong."

"Nothing. Just . . ."

There. His palms framed her face, and his mouth claimed hers with a sudden force that was distinctly un-Alan. She wrapped her arms around his neck, closed her eyes, and willed a little of the magic she so desperately wanted to be there.

In a moment, she didn't have to will the magic. It was simply there. Alan, always so careful with her, always so patient, always so honorable in courting her, turned thief. Impatient, frustrated thief. Heavens, who would have guessed it?

Her head reeled back from the pressure of his mouth. His tongue stole between her lips and dipped inside. That same tongue that had always invited the gentle swirl of tastes now possessively claimed the sweet corners of her mouth with dizzying speed. Her coat buttons flew open; he hadn't asked permission. Neither the cold wind that whipped all around them nor the dark night was as shocking as the feel of Alan's hands roaming willfully under her coat, igniting fires that made her tremble wherever he touched.

"Please" had always been part of his lovemaking before. Not frustration, not urgency, not . . . danger. Never a hint that he could conceivably want her beyond control, never that he was hungry just for her, only for her. New sensations swamped her, emotions she'd never expected. Her unsettled mood disappeared. The night disappeared. Alan disappeared, and the man in his place boldly rubbed a thumb over her nipple; sought the vulnerable pulse in her throat with his mouth; deliberately, provocatively molded her body to the length of his until she could clearly feel his arousal, the heat of him, the primitive need in him.

She shivered violently, and then abruptly he stopped. His mouth lifted from hers, and she could have sworn he was a stranger. Alan's eyes didn't have that smoky glaze; Alan's features never had that threatening harshness; Alan's breath never had that hoarse raspiness. Then, gently, he folded her close and simply held her, forehead to forehead, and he was definitely Alan again.

"I'm sorry, Caro," he whispered. "I didn't mean to frighten you."

"You didn't," she said softly.

Faster than she could believe, he severed the closeness, buttoned her coat, and turned up her collar against the cold. His touch seemed calculated to show her that she was safe, that there had been no marauding thief moments before, that she'd dreamed that Alan. "It's late," he said practically. "Both of us have to be up early in the morning."

"Yes."

"Caro, you know I'd never do anything to hurt you."

"Yes."

"You told me you were free on Saturday. That hasn't changed, has it?"

She shook her head, still bewildered by the lightning-fast change in him, bewildered by feelings he'd ignited that lingered in the shadows like the embers from a fire.

"Maybe—just for fun—we could go look at houses on Saturday. You wanted to see that two-story colonial . . ."

"Yes, I'd love to." They'd been looking at houses on Saturday mornings for weeks now.

He smiled then. "We both drank more champagne than we're used to tonight. That's all it was, Caro. Don't worry about it. I would never rush you. You know that, don't you? And there's nothing to be afraid of. Ever. Not with me." His lips swiftly brushed hers before he turned to open her door.

"Alan . . ."

"No," he said brusquely, as if wary of hearing anything she had to say. "Just sleep well, kitten. And I'll call you tomorrow."

Less than ten minutes later, she was dropping a nightgown over her head. A minute after that the lights were off. But she had trouble falling asleep. In the space of an evening, her safe world had suddenly become unbalanced, threatened. Nothing was the same.

Chapter **2**

ALAN DIPPED A brush into the old-fashioned shaving mug, and then methodically slathered the white foam on his cheeks and throat. A steaming mug of coffee sat on the bathroom vanity next to him. The smells of soap and steam and fresh-brewed coffee were part of the shaving ritual he rarely varied. This Tuesday morning was no different, except that when he lifted the razor to his throat, he glanced at his face in the mirror and abruptly set down the shaving tool.

His eyes were sick with worry. *You're losing her.*

The mirror didn't have much comfort to offer him. The shaving foam couldn't hide an ordinary all-American bone structure, and the shower had slicked back his hair, revealing the hairline he'd inherited from his father . . . and his father, at sixty-four, was bald. Alan had a full head of thick brown hair, but the genetic fate was inescapable. In a couple of decades, he was going to look like Telly Savalas.

But the threat of baldness wasn't the point. His looks just weren't the type to excite a woman. Children and dogs liked his face just fine. In fact, children and dogs followed him around on a regular basis . . . but not women. He had the face of a man who drove a conservative car, wore Brooks Brothers suits, took good care of his parents, and planned to live in a colonial house in the suburbs with 2.2 children and a swing set in the yard.

And that face was a map of the man he was. He liked kids and dogs. He liked his parents. He had no deep dark secrets, no dramatic past, no Paul Newman eyes or Robert Redford saunter to attract a woman. He'd never rushed a woman to bed who wasn't ready, and the first time he'd made love he had suffered more from nerves than his girl had.

None of that would have particularly bothered him, if it hadn't been for Carroll's odd mood the evening before. Truthfully, her unusual behavior hadn't surprised him. Probably he'd been waiting for the ax to begin falling for weeks. He'd seen her studying her sister's fiancé at the party, a man who couldn't be more his diametric opposite. And though Caro couldn't know it, he'd studied Stéphane as thoroughly as she had, right down to his sandalwood and musk after shave.

Alan picked up his razor again, stared at it, and this time firmly set it down. Teeth clamped together, he wiped off the shaving foam with a damp washcloth. His face was clean but whisker-stubbled when he was done. He took a sip of coffee, stared at that beard, and then deliberately walked with the mug in his hand to the bedroom.

After pulling on pants, then a white shirt, he glanced at the clock by his bed. Seven o'clock. In an hour, patients would begin filtering into the office. For Jimmy Johnson, he'd have to put on that ridiculous GI Joe shirt; it was the only way he could get the three-year-old to talk to him, tell him where he was hurting. Other mornings, Alan took that kind of thing with humor. A neurosurgeon could maintain an air

of dignity maybe, but a pediatrician, never. GI
Joe shirts came with the territory; so did He-Man
stickers on his stethoscope, but Alan had no illusions.
A pediatrician wearing Mickey Mouse ears couldn't
compete with a suave, debonair, exciting kind of
man.

Dressed, he finished his coffee, peeled a banana in
the kitchen because he knew darn well his nurse
would demand to know if he'd had breakfast, pock-
eted the article he'd meant to read last night on
Reye's syndrome, and hurried to the car.

The New Yorker's engine was sluggish about getting started, just as he felt. The morning was cold
and dreary; leaves were stuck to his windshield by a
promising-winter wind. Carroll would be getting up
right around now. Her skin was pink-soft early in the
morning; her eyes stayed sleepy until she'd had a second cup of coffee. He knew what she looked like in
the morning because they'd had breakfast together a
dozen times.

They just hadn't slept together.

He'd known the minute he met her that he wanted
to marry Carroll. It wasn't something he could
explain. Like a burst of sunlight, she could suddenly
make him laugh. Like a fire in a winter storm, she
could thaw the chill and weariness of an impossible
day. And like a spear of lightning, she could arouse
him by doing nothing more than sitting in his car,
curled up like a kitten on the seat next to him, a fur
collar brushing her cheek and her eyes softer than
rainbows.

He hadn't pushed to sleep with her because he was
terrified. There was only one other woman he'd ever

considered marrying, a woman who had gradually drifted from his life, moved on to greener pastures. He hadn't necessarily failed with Jena London, because he'd never wanted, needed, or loved her the way he loved Carroll, but now she came back to haunt him.

She'd accused of him of being methodical. He *was* methodical, and when he was with Carroll, he became even more systematic. He'd tried to be extra careful. He didn't want to risk losing her, and Carroll was clearly wary of jumping into an intimate relationship.

"You haven't shaved," June Goodman said the minute he walked in the door.

"Correct," he told his nurse as he took off his coat. "Afraid you'll have to get used to it. I'm growing a beard."

"How nice." June gave him that all-men-occasionally-require-patience smile and followed him into his office. "Did you remember to have breakfast this morning?"

"Of course I had breakfast."

"A *serious* breakfast. Not just a banana."

She fussed around him, showing him the patient files for the day, informing him of lab results that had come in late the previous day. June was fifty-two, stocky, bossy, and occasionally insufferable. He gave her regular raises only because she was irreplaceable.

Finally left in peace, he perched a hip on the edge of his desk and opened the file for Hannah Michaels, a four-year-old who'd been shifted into first place this morning because she had a dangerously high fever.

He tried to concentrate on Hannah, and could only concentrate on Carroll. He'd kept every male hormone under control until those few short minutes last night when frustration had overruled his better sense. When she'd responded like wildfire, she'd startled, delighted, and badly upset him. He'd thought she *wanted* him to control his emotions. He'd been so careful to show her patience, gentleness, affection, respect, to so painstakingly build a relationship before he pressed for sex.

Wasn't that what a woman wanted?

Of course it wasn't what a woman wanted, he thought glumly. Nice men were boring. Nice men weren't . . . heroes. Women wanted romance, excitement, surprises. They didn't want to be saddled for the rest of their lives with a man who was practical and honorable and boring. A woman had a right— and maybe even a need—to be swept off her feet.

Only he didn't know how.

Actually, he didn't have the least idea how.

Learn, said the uncompromising voice in his head. *You've got four days before you see her again . . .*

A quick rap on the door startled him. June's head appeared around the corner. "Hannah's in two." She paused, looking at him. "Have you told Carroll you've decided to grow this beard?"

"No," Alan said irritably, trailing after her.

"Just wondered." June smiled at him as they reached the examining-room door. "You can always shave it off before you see her again," she said reassuringly.

One day, he was likely to throttle the woman for her busy-body ways, but then, he wasn't the throttler type. Which was the point. Types. Types of men. He wasn't the *type* to grow a beard; he wasn't the *type* to seduce a woman. Fact was, maybe over the last two years he'd turned into just a little too much of a fuddy-duddy *type*.

He pushed open the door to the examining room, the child's file in his hand. A frantic young mother was pacing the floor. A tiny girl with far-too-bright eyes and pale cheeks was sitting placidly on the examining table, a Cabbage Patch Kid next to her.

"You can look at my throat, but you have to give *her* all the shots," the little one told him uncompromisingly, pointing at the doll.

Alan didn't miss a beat. "How many do you think she'll need?" he asked gravely.

"Three or two. *I* don't need *any,* though."

He nodded, then put the stethoscope in his ears. "I understand. She's afraid of shots . . . but she's not scared of having me listen to her heart, is she?" he asked.

The child hesitated, then smiled. "She is, but I'm not. You can do me first."

Flexibility, he thought absently. In his work, he'd never had a problem being flexible. And with Carroll —*for* Carroll—he'd simply learn to be.

When the doorbell rang, Carroll hurried through the hall to answer it, still trying to fasten an amber button earring. The catch had always been difficult. She hadn't yet managed it when she opened the door. "I'm so glad you're early; I was just— *Alan?*"

The earring post popped out and bounced on the carpet behind her. She bent down to find it, muttering embarrassed imprecations, with one eye on the scruffy-looking stranger at the door. Alan didn't wear leather moccasins. Or jeans and cord jackets and black shirts open three buttons down over a naked chest. Or sport quarter-inch-long whiskers that implied the man had had a week-long hangover. Or stand like that, looking . . . well . . . *macho*.

But Alan's grin surfaced when he crouched down beside her, immediately finding the amber earring and leaning toward her to fix it in her ear. "Chaotic morning?" he asked gently.

The masculine scents of sandalwood and musk drifted toward her, faint, startling. "Not really. Mom and Nancy both called this morning, both tearing their hair out over this wedding. Then . . ."

Actually, lots had gone wrong with the morning, from trouble with Nancy's wedding plans to a toaster on the blink. Those kinds of problems didn't bother Carroll, but she'd been desperately anxious to see Alan this morning, to make things normal between them again.

She'd had a long week to think since her sister's engagement party . . . and she could have kicked herself since. Like secrets stored in an old attic trunk, she'd discovered a few memories that should have been jettisoned years ago.

Five years ago there'd been another engagement party—her own. At the time, everyone she knew was pairing off; Tom had been part of her life for a year, and they'd both done a good job of telling each other they were in love. The first time in bed should have convinced them otherwise—how dreadful could a first time for any two people be?—but it hadn't.

And the incident at her engagement party had been nothing, just the accident of seeing Tom talking with another woman, laughing in a way he'd never laughed with her, eyes shining as they'd never shone for her . . .

She'd had the sense to give him back his ring, and she'd had the empathy to know just how badly she'd hurt him. So much went into her present wariness of marriage—fear that she hadn't the spark to hold a man for the long term, apprehension that she might thoughtlessly hurt someone else, an awareness that she'd talked herself into believing a relationship existed that never had. Wildly in love, she hadn't been.

Nancy's engagement party had roused all the old fears—foolishly, she saw now. Her relationship with Tom hadn't gone wrong because she hadn't been wildly in love, but because she'd never been honest with herself or him. Only Alan wasn't Tom—how could she have forgotten that? With Alan she *had* been honest. If she didn't feel some crazy-in-love-type nonsense, she at least had a realistic relationship with him, based on love and sharing and mutual interests—everything that really mattered.

And this morning, she wanted nothing more than to show him that she was her sensible self again, a woman with both feet on the ground. Silly moods and old fantasies had been banished for good. Alan deserved better than a woman yearning after pipe-dreams. She offered him her best serene smile . . . just in time for Alan to take sudden advantage of his proximity to give her a kiss.

It was just a hello kiss. Alan always gave her a hello kiss, but his lips felt different today, surrounded by the rough, ticklish beard. And he tasted different, with a roguish promise of mint, and that taste set off a little hum in her head that she hadn't been anticipating at all. As determined as she'd been to start this outing with honesty and common sense and no nonsense, she found her pulse fluttering like a hummingbird's.

"You look beautiful this morning," he told her.

She glanced down, at the old white cords and thick gold sweater she'd donned for their Saturday morning outing. She didn't look beautiful. Her hair might look extra nice, but that was hardly enough to rate the compliment. And if she'd been dressed in sequins, she doubted that Alan would normally have noticed. Speechless for a second and a half, she responded carefully, "Alan, are you feeling all right?"

"Just fine." He motioned boyishly to his chin. "Like the beard?"

"Hmmm," she said expressively. First thing in the morning was no time to hurt anyone's feelings. She'd never deliberately hurt Alan's feelings.

She had little time to mull over the beard, because Alan was thumbing through her hall closet, getting her coat for her. "I know I promised you we'd look at that colonial house, but there's another place I'd like you to see, too. You've got the whole afternoon free, haven't you?"

"Yes." For a minute, she couldn't imagine why he was standing there holding her kid jacket open. Belatedly, she realized he was doing it for her. Heavens.

Swiftly, she slipped into it, a flush on her cheeks that deepened when his hands slipped inside her collar, smoothing it when it didn't need smoothing, touching her in such a way that his fingers caressed the soft skin at the nape of her neck.

Breathless, she slipped ahead of him outside, with one last glance at her pumpkin and cream living room. She'd planned on making fresh coffee and serving him doughnuts, because Alan loved doughnuts, but somehow it didn't seem the time. It just didn't have the feel of an average Saturday morning.

She *knew* it wasn't the average Saturday morning when she looked in the apartment's lot for Alan's New Yorker and saw only a metallic red Fiero. "Alan?"

"Just bought it," he affirmed. "Like her, Caro?"

Climbing into the soft leather seat, glancing at the complicated dials and five on the floor, she wondered where on earth one would put a bag of groceries, much less the stack of medical journals and doctor's bag Alan always carried with him. "Very sporty," she answered. "You sold the New Yorker?"

"Not yet, but I will," Alan said lightly as he put the car in gear and backed up. "It just occurred to me what a practical, sensible car that was. You didn't think I was always practical and sensible, did you, Caro?"

Yes. "No," she said hesitantly. It wasn't like her to lie, but she needed a minute to absorb the meaning of all these changes. As it was, she was still trying to catch her breath.

"One can overdo the responsible image. There's

more to life than being serious." Abruptly, he shot her a grin. "We're going to have fun today, and that's a promise." .

The pulse in her throat slowed down to a normal rate. Alan's grin was as familiar as apple pie. "We always have fun when we're together," Carroll said affectionately.

"More fun, then. Completely forget work and responsibilities and just let it happen."

"Sounds good," she murmured.

Lafayette's city streets zoomed past, abetted by a purring engine and a cornering speed that had her reaching for her seat belt. The gray-green waters of the Wabash River glittered beneath them, and then they were in West Lafayette, winging past Purdue . . . Carroll stole glances at Alan at every turn.

House hunting on Saturday mornings was just one of the casual pastimes they'd taken up recently. Alan had always chosen outings that suited their mutual needs and interests. Their compatibility was real, and she wasn't likely to forget that again . . . but this morning felt increasingly different from their other dates. The changes in Alan were rather baffling.

Not necessarily upsetting or alarming, but definitely baffling. Usually comfortable with Alan, she felt an odd blend of anticipation and nervousness today. It was almost as if she were going out with a stranger, dating someone for the first time.

Sandalwood and musk, the beard, the black chamois shirt, jeans that hugged his long, muscular legs, the lingering flavor of that morning kiss . . . he wasn't Alan. Not that she went for a scruffy appearance, but his look was rather unexpectedly and boldly male.

And in the close confines of the sports car, she felt a trickle of something chase up and down her spine, something starkly sexual, something elemental and powerful . . .

His hand suddenly reached over and claimed hers. "Cold, honey?"

She linked fingers with him, welcoming the comfort of his big hand enclosing her smaller one. "Not at all." There, now. Alan wasn't a dangerous stranger, but the considerate man he'd always been. She relaxed, as she always relaxed around Alan. So he'd had a masculine whim when he got dressed that morning. Well, all men who could afford it probably succumbed to the yen for a sports car sometime.

It was the best of October mornings, cool and crisp, with sunlight so bright it turned the leaves to garnet and amber and emerald. City turned into country, with roads that wound around sleepy hills and ancient woods.

Lafayette wasn't the kind of town that boomed or died out on the whim of the economy. Having survived the rule of the British, Indians, and French a few centuries before, the residents had learned to roll with the punches. Suburbs didn't just pop up in Lafayette. New houses were more likely to go up in twos and threes, some in the country and some in the city, all constructed with the understanding that they were going to last.

When Alan stopped the car, he said quietly, "Now, I know this one sounded like something we'd both like, Caro. But keep an open mind until I show you a second one later today, all right?"

"Of course."

But she loved the area the minute she stepped out of the car. A contractor was putting up four homes, all two-story colonial-style houses with huge yards, nestled among the hills. It wasn't far from town, yet kids could easily and safely play here, and one had the illusion of getting away from it all while at the same time neighbors were only a few steps away.

There was no grass yet, and the sidewalk was littered with sawdust. They went inside the first house, still so new there were no windows, no doors, and the floors on the second level weren't completed. It smelled like fresh wood and newness, like hopes and dreams. Carroll just looked at Alan, whatever worries she'd previously had dissolving instantly.

He chuckled. "Caro, you like every house we see," he chided.

"I can't help it. Just look at the fireplace!" She wandered over to the fieldstone hearth. "I can just imagine a fire here, a Christmas tree in that corner..." She stuffed her hands into her jacket pockets and ambled through the rooms. "Alan, this is a wonderful kitchen!"

He followed her, leaning against the doorway. Chunks of space had been left for appliances, but the kitchen was no more than wishful thinking at this point. The cabinets were oak, and still unvarnished. A space had been marked for an island counter. Windows looked onto a showy cluster of trees in fall colors. He saw all that, but couldn't stop looking at Caro.

If anyone had accused her of being a dreamer, she would have instantly denied it, but Caro *was* a dreamer. When she looked at the windows, he knew she was mentally putting up curtains. When she opened a cupboard, he knew she was mentally stocking it. Thanksgiving turkeys were being carved on the counter, dishes put away on a hurried morning, coffee being poured at an invisible table after a long day's work . . . Caro was doing all of that, just standing there with her hands in her pockets, her spaniel-brown eyes sparkling, her lips parted in a grin. "I can't stand it," she said.

"I know you can't."

"I love it, Alan!" Her eyes narrowed. "But we haven't seen the bedrooms. They're probably dreadful little cracker boxes . . ."

She was off, Alan following her. The stairway was in; she took the steps two at a time. "Watch it up there," he cautioned, knowing darn well he'd promised himself to drill caution right out of his character, but this was different. The upstairs was little more than bare beams.

Balancing on those bare beams, Carroll carefully made her way from room to room upstairs. "Two bathrooms," she called back. "Master bedroom with a *huge* closet; good heavens, you could put a bed in there. The view from the second bedroom's kind of blah, but, oh, Alan . . ."

She paused between two rough boards at the opening to the last bedroom. It was tiny, with an alcove window and a view of the far hills. A crib belonged in that alcove. Anyone who didn't put a crib in there would have to be crazy. A crib with a soft yellow ruffle and a cuddly bear and a mobile that played

Brahms. The carpet would be white—when she was dreaming she didn't have to be practical—and next to the crib she would place a big, old-fashioned rocker with arms, the kind that was really meant to rock a baby...

Alan's arms slipped around her from behind. His chin nestled on the top of her head, coaxing her back to the warmth of his chest. "What are you seeing?" he murmured.

"Just . . . a baby's room." She half turned to look at him, still snuggled in his arms. "The thing is, Alan, what if the wrong people got hold of this house? What if they did something idiotic like make this room into a *den?*"

She said the word as if it were a cuss. Amused, Alan said gently, "You liked the Cape Cod–style house we looked at last week just as much."

"I couldn't have."

"You did. And remember when I asked you to keep an open mind this morning? Come on, Caro . . ."

He helped her down the stairs and outside. She stole one last glance at the house as he urged her into the car. A few miles later, the Fiero sped under an ancient, wood-covered bridge that creaked and groaned; abruptly they were in wilder country.

Carroll glanced at Alan, unsure where they could possibly be headed, but there was no clue to their destination in Alan's slash of a smile. "Patience," he urged.

He wasn't sure if he was urging patience for himself or for her. He, too, had seen that imaginary baby in the alcove. Their baby. Cradled in Carroll's arms. And he had to whip that image out of his mind before it settled there. That was last week's way of thinking —babies and colonial houses and marriage.

That was dull thinking, the kind of thing nice, boring, sedate, fuddy-duddies dreamed of. Not men with extravagant imaginations and adventurous characters and flexible values. Alan wanted more for Carroll than a stereotyped future, and he was just coming to understand that maybe he wanted more for himself as well.

In time, he pulled onto a sloped gravel path and parked at the crest of a knoll. Beyond birds and squirrels, there wasn't a sign of life. Ahead of them loomed a massive old red barn, with a Pennsylvania Dutch hex sign painted on the roll-open doors. Carroll looked at him bewilderedly.

"Now wait, just wait . . ." Alan climbed out of the car and reached in the back for the box and blanket he'd crammed into the Fiero's tiny storage space. "Follow me. And don't jump to any conclusions until I've explained. Here."

Alan tossed her the wool blanket. She caught it and trailed after him as he jammed a shoulder into the barn door and pushed. With a haunted creak, it opened.

"Now come on in . . ."

The barn was dark. It smelled like old leather and old wood and cold. Two lofts overlooked the main floor, which was empty except for a pile of loose straw—hay? who knew the difference?—in one corner. On the first level, there was ample space to hold a county fair. The beamed ceiling stretched as high as the sky, and a sparrow—evidently confused —was winging back and forth from one beam to another.

"Alan," Carroll started hesitantly. This was it? The second "house" they were going to look at? This was *it?*

Chapter 3

ALAN NUDGED A glass of champagne into Carroll's hand. She would have thanked him if her vocal cords had been functional. As it was, the power of speech had deserted her. So had Alan. He was spreading the wool blanket on the pile of straw. The champagne had appeared from the box he'd just opened, and next to the wine stood a tin of beluga caviar and a box of wafer-thin crackers.

She gulped three sips of the sparkling wine, stared at Alan, and swallowed another gulp. Champagne and caviar for lunch?

He seriously had in mind living in a barn?

Was this Alan, or did he have a twin brother recently escaped from a mental institution?

She took another sip of wine, and would certainly have finished the glass if Alan hadn't taken it from her. In its place, he handed her a cracker mounded high with Russian black roe. "Now," he said with satisfaction, "we can talk."

"I think we'd better," she said faintly.

"But *not* standing up. First we get comfortable."

He motioned her down to the blanket. As far as comfort went, the wool blanket was scratchy and the straw unyielding, but none of this was of immediate concern to Carroll. Alan stretched out next to her and propped himself up on an elbow. In contrast to the startled alarm in her own eyes, Alan's reflected the cool blue of a fathomless pond.

"Caro," he said gently, "most people seem to want a two-story colonial house in a suburb. It's a predictable choice, a sensible, logical choice."

"Yes." She couldn't say much more. He'd urged the cracker to her lips, and her taste buds were exploding under the unexpected saltiness of the delicacy.

"We've been looking at houses for weeks, because we like to look at houses, because we both like to imagine what it would be like to live with different floor plans and layouts and in different areas. Yes?"

"Yes," she agreed.

"Yes," Alan echoed, "but last week it occurred to me that we're forgetting to dream, Caro. And that standard traditional houses may be someone else's dream. What about a place that could be made totally individual to us? A nest for just our dreams and no one else's. Are you listening?"

She was listening, or perhaps feeling more than listening. Alan was serious. She couldn't remember ever having seen quite that brooding intensity in his expression. A shock of hair brushed his temples, out of place. His palm drifted from her cheek to her throat, where his thumb idly stroked the soft underside of her chin. He was looking at her . . . possessively. Alan never looked at her possessively.

"A barn seems pretty unlikely at first, doesn't it?" he said quietly. "But look closer, honey." He leaned back, drew her into the crook of his shoulder and motioned toward the roof. "Can you picture a double skylight up there, on both sides of the beams? And a huge stone fireplace in the center of the room. Can't you imagine sleeping up there in one of the open lofts, with a view of the stars above and the warmth and glow of a fire below?"

She wanted to share the whimsical dream, but it was hard. A cold wind was whistling through the barn boards, and there were cobwebs strung from beam to beam. "A person could fall out of those open lofts pretty easily," she said hesitantly.

"We'd have railings."

"What about bathrooms?"

"We'd have bathrooms, too."

"Where?"

"Anywhere you want to put them."

"Heaven knows, there's room for ten bathrooms downstairs alone," she murmured.

Maybe insanity was catching, because she could almost imagine the massive old barn being transformed into a house. Homey—never. But with paint and partitions and windows and carpets . . . She tried to envision it as a home, for Alan's sake. For the moment it seemed less important to worry about what had brought on his drastic personality change than to tend to the crisis at hand. Alan was looking at her. He seemed to need something important from her, something she couldn't fathom.

She pushed the lock of hair from the temples of her stranger. "Alan, are you serious about this?"

"You know exactly what I'm serious about?"

"What?"

"I want a place for you to dream, Caro. A place for you to be absolutely anyone you want to be. We can make a nest anywhere . . . on the beach, in a city, in a barn. It takes something more elemental than walls and windows to bring two people together, and we both know that. But what I'd like for you is a place where you feel free to let down your hair, not care about the rules, about responsibilities. Admit it, sweet. Life teaches us all to be cautious, but that isn't really what we want to be. That isn't what *you* really want to be, now, is it?"

"No . . ." She felt the faintest warmth color her cheeks, as if she'd confessed to the deepest, most intimate secret with that single word. It was so true, though. At times she'd felt trapped by the lessons life taught her, aware she was overly cautious and maybe too careful. No one wanted to bungle through life asking to be hurt . . . but she'd never wanted to be inhibited with Alan. Did he understand?

The sleepy blue of his eyes somehow promised her he did. A dozen words surged to her lips, all wanting to escape at the same time. For forever she'd wanted to be honest with him, man to woman honest, intimately honest about secrets and fears and dreams. Maybe it was the craziness of the barn, or the champagne, or the unique flavor of the caviar, but she suddenly understood that she could have that kind of honesty with Alan if she just reached for it.

And he was so close. He shifted, leaning over her. The pad of his thumb gently traced the shape of her bottom lip. "Where did you get those beautiful brown eyes?" he murmured.

"Pardon?"

Alan's gaze slid from her eyes to her lips. She could feel him staring at her lips as one of his hands slowly reached down and undid the top button of her jacket. Then the second button. Then the third.

"Safe can be nice," he murmured gently. "In fact, I think that's what first attracted you to me, wasn't it, Caro? You've always felt safe with me. But maybe . . . you really never wanted to feel all that safe. And just maybe, it never occurred to you that the two of us are capable of something quite . . . dangerous together."

Again she tried to say something, but words failed her.

Alan smiled with satisfaction, just before his mouth covered hers.

Surrounded by the tattered scruff of beard, his lips were infinitely beguiling, wooing her down, deeper into the blanket. A swallow sang somewhere. Sandalwood and cold crisp air and the scent of straw assaulted her senses in a rush, as if no other smells had ever existed. A hum filled her ears with a whispered song about yearning and desire and magic. It was crazy, really.

Alan's tongue stole inside her mouth. Tongue tips touched; hers initially retreated. They were in a barn, she tried to remind herself. She had to muster up a little sense. It was midmorning. It wasn't the right time of day. And Alan would certainly never . . .

It seemed that Alan certainly would, because his fingers unfastened the last button of her jacket. His hand slipped inside, pushed up her heavy wool sweater, and in one smooth motion unlatched the front hook of her bra. For a moment, Carroll was distracted by the faintest whiff of feminine outrage. Where had he acquired the expertise to unlatch front-hooked bras like that? She'd never worn one before; the wisp of violet lace was brand-new . . . but then, a lot of things suddenly felt brand-new. Dangerously, deliciously new.

Her breasts, for instance. Women were supposed to be so sexually sensitive around their breasts. Carroll had never felt that special sensitivity; it was simply nice, being touched. Alan's thumb deliberately rubbed the nipple, teasing the tip with pressure and then softness, and suddenly "nice" had nothing to do with the throbbing sensations affecting her pulse. The tingles traveling up her spine were distinctly . . . wicked. Her breath caught, was immediately captured by Alan's kiss.

A lifetime later, he raised his lips, only to let them wander back down to her neck, then up to the shell of her ear. "I think," he murmured, "you're not feeling quite so safe right now, are you, Caro?"

"Alan—" An awful lot of moorings were shifting all at once.

"I think"—his lips dipped to her throat—"it might have been a mistake ever to let you feel safe, love. You're not, you know. We're alone here. There's no one anywhere around for miles. And you'd better understand right now that I've wanted to touch you this way for so long . . ."

His head ducked down again, at the same time as his hand wandered from her abdomen to her thighs. Through her thin white cords, she could feel the heat of his palm, the deliberate sensual pressure. Desire trickled through her bloodstream, unexpected, deliciously enticing. Wanting had never been so easy to feel, to express, to share.

His palms cupped her breasts together. His tongue lashed at their tips until the nipples were red and hot. His tongue was so soft that the graze of beard surrounding his mouth seemed impossibly rough, sensuously rough.

He rubbed his cheek against her vulnerable flesh, first against satin-soft breasts and then against the smoothness of her stomach. Air hissed from her lungs. Adrenaline—or maybe melted butter—raced through her veins. Danger licked through her senses . . . but so did a languid, sultry feeling of pure feminine power. The Alan-would-nevers had changed in her mind to the very sure knowledge that she could well be taken on the floor of a barn, by a man she suddenly realized she didn't know at all. More terrifying than that, she wasn't sure she cared!

Her knees, locked together, were gently, firmly separated when his hand slipped between them. He stroked the inside of her thigh, where she'd always been the most vulnerable, where Alan couldn't possibly know she'd always been the most vulnerable. She twisted around him, unsure whether she was trying to press closer to him or stop his hands from their marauding forays. It didn't stop him. His mouth molded itself fiercely to hers at the same time his palm made a shelf at the juncture of her thighs, and he rubbed until she arched for the feel of his hand, abandon rippling through her like a storm.

Gradually, slowly, Alan decreased the pressure, gently gliding his hand back to her thigh, her hip, around to the soft flesh of her stomach. As he would gentle a wild creature, he gentled the woman breathing so hoarsely beneath him.

He kissed each white breast one last time, then reclasped her bra and pulled down the sweater and kissed her again, on her throat, her cheek, her closed eyelids. The tension in his groin was painful, distracting him when he didn't want to be distracted. He wanted to savor the flush on Caro's cheeks, the trembling of her mouth, the sensual darkness in her eyes when her lashes fluttered open. He'd never seen Caro like this. He'd never dreamed how special, how beautiful, how vulnerable she was in loving.

There was a word for a woman who teased. There was probably a word for a man as well. Unfortunately, he'd have to live with the epithet, because he'd just had an infinitely clear glimpse of how it could be for them, how he wanted it to be for Carroll when they made love for the first time.

The caviar and wine had been so easy. He could think up more ways to court her as a woman wanted to be courted. He'd been selfish, he realized, too set in his ways to see Carroll's needs—but that was all going to change. *He* was going to change—completely.

"Caro?" Reluctantly, he leaned away from her to reach for the bottle of champagne and tin of caviar. When he handed her a cracker and a glass of wine, their eyes met, and he couldn't help but smile. Carroll was lying limply on the blanket, and her brown eyes still looked dazed. "Would you like to go dancing tonight?" he asked her.

"Dancing?" The word seemed unfamiliar. The world seemed vaguely unfamiliar. She couldn't stop looking at Alan, even as she sipped the wine, even as she nibbled at the caviar.

Her breasts felt a lingering, exhilarating awareness from the intimate chafing of his beard. The caviar suddenly tasted saltier. The air was fresher, the smell of straw stronger than before. A feeling of wonder felt as fragile as a secret inside her, intensified by a growing awareness that Alan had feelings for her that she'd never guessed before.

The wine and caviar and loving came at her all at once, as something he'd planned uniquely for her. If he'd intended for her to feel special, she definitely did. More special, more alive, more *woman* than she'd felt in forever.

Alan clicked glasses with her, winked with a winsome grin. "Dancing," he repeated. "As in—until dawn, Caro. Tonight, if you're free?"

"Yes, but, Alan? I always thought . . . you didn't like to dance."

He motioned that detail aside with a wave of his hand and took a long swallow of wine, his gaze flickering absently around the barn. "Do you see what I mean about this place now, honey?"

Carroll restudied her surroundings, this time barely noticing the cobwebs and chill and bare boards. Maybe they were still there, but they didn't seem to matter as much. All her life, she'd been determined to be practical. At this moment, she could envision a palace in a treehouse. "An endless feeling of spaciousness," she commented blissfully.

"It would definitely be a house like no one else's."

"Absolutely. And character, Alan. The whole place has character." Alan threw back his head and laughed, and Carroll cocked her head at him curiously. "What's so funny?"

"Oh . . . nothing's funny, exactly. I'm just so relieved you like the place, can see the same potential in it that I do, Caro. When you first walked in, I could see you had doubts."

"A few, maybe—but none that seem so terribly important now," she said softly, although she wasn't sure she was referring to the barn.

"Good," Alan said with satisfaction, "because I bought the property yesterday."

A dollop of caviar suddenly went down Carroll's throat the wrong way. Alan thumped her on the back until the coughing spasm passed.

Wedding invitations were spread out on Carroll's kitchen table, along with the Sunday paper, a roll of stamps, coffee mugs, and extravagant lists of potential guests. Nancy finished a lengthy dissertation on her fiancé's travel plans, from Stéphane's flight back to Quebec to his expected return two days before the wedding. When that failed to get Carroll's attention, she tried talking clothes, and when that failed, she just shook her head. "I hate to say this," Nancy said politely, "but I'm supposed to be the scatterbrained one in this family, with Mom running a close second."

"And?" Carroll licked a stamp, stabbed it at the envelope, and looked up.

"You've addressed three envelopes to the James Parker family. Far as I know, we only have to invite them one time, and then only because Mom'll have a fit if I don't."

"Did I really?" Carroll looked appropriately amazed, then yawned sleepily.

"How late were you up last night anyway?" Nancy asked suspiciously.

"Till four-thirty."

"A.M.?"

"You've got it."

"And does that time bear some relationship to the fact that you're wearing only one slipper?"

"I have a blister on the other foot," Carroll explained reasonably. It was on her right toe, and not very big. Blisters were never any fun, but if one had to get one, dancing all night was definitely the way to do it.

Drinking champagne while dancing all night was an even better way. And doing both with Alan . . .

Abruptly realizing that her sister was staring at her with an annoyingly patronizing grin, Carroll shuffled a half-dozen wedding invitations in front of her and efficiently sifted through her mother's guest list. "We've got to get to work," she said firmly.

"One of us *was* working. You're the one who keeps mentally wandering off." Nancy added in a murmur, "How the mighty do fall."

"Pardon?"

"Nothing. It's just nice to see that you can be as batty as the rest of us."

"Does this conversation make no sense at all, or is it me?" Carroll wondered aloud.

"It's you," Nancy assured her. "I assume it's Alan who's done this to you?"

"Done what to me?"

"That's exactly what I mean. You don't even know." Nancy shook her head in despair.

Carroll stood up and hobbled over to the stove for

more coffee. "I haven't the least idea what you're
talking about. I've known the man for months. He
hasn't done anything to me."

"*Something* has changed you in the last few days."

"Nonsense."

"You're going out with him tonight?"

Carroll nodded. "And on Thursday. He's speaking
to a medical group, a banquet at Purdue where he has
to give a talk."

Nancy scrunched up her nose. "Sounds dull."

"You've never been to *anything* as dull as a medical convention," Carroll agreed happily.

"There, now. My sister just made an almost rational statement for the first time this morning," Nancy
said to thin air. "Maybe she hasn't got as bad a case
as I thought."

"Do you have any idea," Carroll said thoughtfully,
"how many times I nearly emergolated you when we
were kids?"

Nancy chuckled. Carroll, having forgotten the
coffee, found herself in front of the kitchen cupboard
that held the aspirin. Popping two, she followed them
up with a water chaser. Contrary to what her sister
kept implying, the only things wrong with her this
morning were a total lack of sleep, a teeny blister,
and a slight headache caused by having consumed a
ridiculous amount of champagne the night before.

All of which had been worth it.

Darn it, who would have guessed Alan could even
think up such enticing things, much less whisper
them in her ear on a crowded dance floor?

A little nagging voice in the back of her head kept
harassing her to take a second look at things. Realis-

tically, for instance, a man didn't change from day to night at will. Realistically, she wasn't absolutely positive by light of day that she wanted to live in a barn. Realistically, she was a little shocked to discover she'd nearly been seduced in a bed of straw on a Saturday morning. Realistically, she wasn't absolutely sure with whom she'd danced cheek to cheek for an entire night, because the Alan she knew panicked at weddings for the obligatory waltz with the bride.

Her eyes turned dreamy, staring at the water in her glass. Realism belonged on *Sixty Minutes*. Who cared? She'd be sensible again tomorrow. Today she was too busy relishing secrets. For so long she'd been afraid that the chemistry was tepid between them, that Alan never really saw her as a woman, that desire was something she would never experience . . .

"Caro?" Nancy's voice was patient.

"Hmmm?"

"Are we going to let the front doorbell keep ringing, or would you like me to get it?"

Carroll blinked. "Oh—I will." She straightened and headed for the door, but when she opened it, there was no one there—just five long slim boxes lying on her doormat. Frowning, she gathered them up and used her hip to close the door against the bitter wind.

"Good heavens!" Nancy hurried forward to catch a box before it fell. "What *is* this?"

"I haven't any idea." Juggling them on the way to the kitchen, Carroll tried to search for a card, but couldn't find one. Finally, she pulled the ribbon off the first box and parted the folds of green tissue paper. Her breath caught. A dozen long-stemmed white roses were lying there, infinitely fragile.

"Good Lord!" Nancy, laughing, started pulling ribbons every which way. Each box held a dozen roses, each a different color. Red, white, coral, yellow, pink . . . "I hope to heavens you have a ton of vases, and I can't imagine how he got these delivered on a Sunday morning," Nancy said breathlessly. "Carroll, where did you find this extravagant man? These cost a fortune! I've never even seen that coral color in a rose . . ."

Neither had Carroll, but it was a single white rose she lifted from the first box. A glisten of moisture shimmered on one soft petal, enhancing the most subtle of fragrances, the delicate scent of the bud.

Her heart was suddenly beating tick-tock-tick like a clock. In one world, she chattered to Nancy as the two combed the apartment for vases, glasses, any containers that could hold water. In the other world, she never let go of the white rose, and her heart kept beating, and for some ridiculous reason her hands felt trembly. Alan did this? *Alan?*

She suddenly couldn't remember a single reason why she had to be sensible, or rational, or logical, or practical. So she'd been that way all her life. So she'd thought they had a strictly common-sense relationship, based solely on shared values and common goals and not at all on whimsical gestures, not on . . . romance. So the sudden change in Alan had raised a few uneasy worries at the back of her mind . . .

The man was entitled to change.

Nothing and no one was going to make her give up the white rose.

On Thursday at four, when Alan was supposed to pick her up for the medical banquet, June Goodman called Carroll from his office.

"Crisis time," the nurse said flatly. "I know the man hasn't called you, nor has he had a minute to look at his speech. Mind you, I didn't schedule a single appointment after two, but it's been one of those afternoons. Two sets of stitches, a little tyke with an asthma attack, and I've still got two in the waiting room. It's going to take a bomb to get him out of here, and even that may not work."

Carroll chuckled. Months before, she'd met June. They hadn't formed an instant friendship so much as a natural conspiracy. June was a born conspirator. "All right," she said lightly. "I'll pick him up there to save time, no problem."

Within a half-hour, Carroll had zoomed to town, purchased a man's shirt from a department store, driven to Alan's office, and was striding inside. Some women might be irritated to be neither called nor picked up for a date, particularly if they had spent money on a new mauve silk dress, dangling earrings, and eyeshadow. Carroll had accepted the pitfalls of dating a pediatrician from the beginning.

Actually, however strange the situation might be, her step was lighter than it had been all week. Yes, she'd adored the roses. For that matter, she could easily become addicted to caviar, and she'd loved dancing until dawn . . . but the roses and Fiero and beard and champagne all together had been just a little overwhelming. Walking on air was wonderful, but the chance to put her feet on the ground again wasn't so bad. It wasn't typical of Alan to be inconsiderate, but it was typical of him to be so involved in his work that he forgot to eat. That was the Alan she'd always known.

June looked up with a cheerful smile when she walked in. "I have to warn you, he's still got that beard."

"Hmmm." Carroll noted one more patient in the waiting room, a little girl curled up in her mother's lap. She glanced at her watch. "He'll still get to the banquet in time for his speech if we can hustle him out of here within an hour."

"Make that *you*, not *we*."

"Has he been a bear today?" Carroll asked sympathetically, but she didn't stop to talk. Alan's office was just behind the reception area. She whisked through the door, slipped off her coat, and removed the new shirt from the shopping bag. Plain blue— Alan had always liked plain blue. Not that he needed a new shirt, but he wouldn't have time to go home and change at this late hour. Once she had hung up the shirt and shaken out the creases, she wandered to his desk. His speech had to be buried somewhere in the chaos of papers.

"Beautiful dress," June complimented from the doorway.

"Thank you." Carroll cocked her head with a smile. "A little risqué, I'm afraid . . . particularly for a medical convention. I don't know what got into me." Except the roses. If Alan thought she merited five dozen roses, just once she'd wanted a dress to fit the image. The bodice was wrapped into a V at the throat and held together by a single button at the side of her waist. The skirt flowed when she walked, occasionally revealing more of her legs than the future wife of a pediatrician probably should. The future wife of a pediatrician also probably shouldn't have sprayed cologne between her breasts or left her bra at home, but there it was. The roses had done something to her judgment, and she looked at June with sudden uncertainty.

"You'll knock his socks off," June said placidly. "Exactly what that boy needs. For two weeks now, he's been in the strangest mood . . ."

Carroll knew; however, it wasn't the new Alan who strode out of the examining room with a toddler in his arms but the old one. Tired lines were creased around his eyes; his white jacket was wrinkled and dotted with Masters of the Universe stickers. Holding the four-year-old on one arm, he was clearly trying to transform a Transformer with the other, talking to the little boy all the while. "I give up," he admitted to the tyke.

"You can't help it if you aren't as smart as me."

"True," Alan said gravely. "But we've got a deal, don't we? You stay in bed all day tomorrow, and your mom gets you another Transformer."

"You really wrote that on the pres'tion pad?" the boy asked suspiciously.

"Of course I did. See?" Alan read from a small white prescription form. "One Transformer that turns into a dinosaur."

"Swoop," the little boy helpfully supplied the

name of the Transformer.

"Ah." Alan handed him back his toy, grabbed a pen and added "Swoop" to his prescription. Minutes later, Alan handed the little one to his mother and caught sight of Carroll in the doorway. His face showed a transparent array of emotions—mostly guilt. "Hell, Carroll, I did call you to tell you I'd be late, didn't I?"

"Just take care of your last patient," she told him.

Fifteen minutes later, everyone was gone but the two of them, and Alan was behind the open door of his bathroom. A hand appeared holding his doctor's white jacket. Carroll took it. Then his old shirt, well wrinkled, and she took that, too. When he strode out buttoning his new shirt, he was scowling. "The last thing I feel like is going to a medical convention. Much less giving a speech I haven't even had time to prepare."

"Yes." She handed him his tie.

"Nor do I want to drag you to this thing. You know darn well it'll be boring."

"Yes."

"And the food will be terrible."

"Yes."

"The whole thing is a ridiculous waste of time."

"Of course it is." This was just so very much Alan, who hadn't noticed her dress yet, who hadn't the least interest in being a keynote speaker for anything, and who was cranky as a bear when he forgot to eat lunch—and she knew darn well he'd forgotten to eat lunch. The tiny invisible worries that had been nagging her all week abruptly disappeared. Her heart swelled, loving him. This was a man she knew she could live her life with.

She took his speech—he would have forgotten it —and flicked out the last light, because he would have forgotten that, too. At the door, he suddenly turned, dropped a surprise kiss on her mouth, and said worriedly, "Did I bring this shirt to work this morning?"

She hid a chuckle, and briskly ordered him out the door before they were late.

How silly . . . to worry for even a minute that he'd seriously changed from the man she'd loved and trusted.

Chapter 4

ALAN TOOK ONE appalled look at the crowded hall and promptly muttered, "Good Lord. There must be a private corner someplace."

Just as promptly, he was surrounded by his colleagues. Amused—why Alan persisted in believing he couldn't handle a crowd was beyond her—Carroll found the punch bowl and wandered at a lingering pace from one conversational group to another. Coping with strangers had never bothered her; she liked meeting people. A few doctors were wearing smiles as starched as their shirts, but most of them were friendly, caring people. Wives drew together to air their complaints about being married to doctors, and the doctors' talk was primarily about medicine, with a little golf thrown in.

The type of gathering was familiar; Carroll had attended medical conferences with Alan before. Most of the people were strangers, but strangers never stayed that way for long when coaxed to talk about themselves.

This dinner was a fund-raiser—not Alan's cup of tea, but its purpose was to bring together medical personnel from Indiana and three of the surrounding states to share resources and ideas for a new children's facility. Alan cared about the subject; so did

Carroll. The roast beef was almost tasteless, but generally she enjoyed herself.

Just before his speech, the thinnest bead of nervous perspiration formed on Alan's brow. When his name was announced, Carroll was left alone to watch him make his way to the dais. She knew he was nervous; it didn't show. He stood tall, for a man who wasn't overly tall. His beard was beginning to look less scruffy; his suit fit his broad shoulders perfectly; and his voice resonated with the passionate commitment he had made to children . . . Really, she was hopelessly proud of him.

The applause afterward demonstrated the respect he'd earned from his colleagues. Carroll could see he was oblivious to it; he hurried back to her side and seated himself, murmuring an irritable, "Thank God that's over. We should be able to escape here in another hour."

Carroll wasn't in a hurry to leave. All week long, she'd lapped up the attentions Alan had showered on her, like a hedonist basking in the sun on an island paradise. At core, though, she wasn't such a hedonist, just a woman who needed to know she was more than a convenient fixture for the man in her life.

She *was* more than a fixture, and she had no permanent craving for caviar. Outings like this gave Alan a chance to share professional problems and interests, and she didn't want him rushing away because of her. She saw proof of his commitment in the way Alan reacted when a tall, white-haired man paused at their table.

"Dr. Whinaker!" Alan said with pleasure.

The men exchanged handshakes, and then Carroll

found her palm enclosed in the older man's warm grasp. She gathered quickly that Alan knew the man from his medical school days in Chicago, and that the doctor's regard was important to him. Her spine straightened imperceptibly.

"... was hoping to catch you and mention that staff position to you again, Alan. A few years back, you were sure you'd be happy with a small private practice ..."

"Not so small anymore, actually."

Though Dr. Whinaker used the conversation to sneak in hints of an available staff position for Alan, the dialogue that flew back and forth was more than that. Carroll thought with amusement that most old friends meeting again would want to do some catching up on their personal lives, but these two men appeared eager to share details of every difficult case they'd had in the intervening years. A welter of medical terms zipped back and forth. Alan tested the older man's judgment just as thoroughly as the older doctor probed Alan's.

Smiling and content, Carroll finished her coffee and enjoyed watching them. That they liked and respected each other was obvious—which made it all the more startling when Alan's hand suddenly locked on her wrist.

He stood up, drawing Carroll with him, ignoring her startled look. "I wish I had more time to talk with you, Dr. Whinaker. Maybe we can get together soon?"

Alan couldn't escape without a few more words, and then there were greetings and good-byes to be fielded before he could successfully maneuver the two of them to the door. He handled the exchanges with efficient, methodical precision, and only wished he'd handled the rest of the evening as well.

Guilt had hit him during the roast beef course. Irritation with himself had accelerated from there. He'd completely blown it earlier. He'd meant to tell Carroll she looked stunning, not to be preoccupied with the dozen patients he'd seen that day. He'd meant to ask her about her work and really listen, not to be forced to review his damn speech in the car. He'd never intended to ignore her in the crowd; he'd forgotten to mention her dress . . . Oh, hell, he'd done everything wrong. He'd meant to be completely unlike himself, to surprise her, entice her, romance her . . .

"Alan?" Carroll, bewildered by the breathless rush through the crowd, could barely catch her breath. Alan whisked her past the coat racks, through an all but deserted hall. "What happened? Is something wrong?"

"Just bear with me, would you? This is important."

His voice was terse; a quick frown of both concern and surprise marred her brow, but she immediately matched his long stride. As if the devil were after them, he urged her up a flight of stairs.

The faculty rooms were upstairs, all closed up and locked; the hallway lights were on half-power, and their footsteps echoed up and down the deserted corridor like lonely ghosts. At the first totally dark doorway, he ducked inside and pulled her with him.

He released the tight grip on her hand, and suddenly smiled, a slow, lazy smile. "Hi," he murmured.

"Hi?"

She wasn't expecting *Hi*. Or that sudden winsome smile of his. Or to be pinned against a wall in a deserted hallway. Still trying to catch her breath, she felt the oddest sudden nervousness, and was vaguely aware that her fingers were trying to fuss with her collar. Only her dress didn't have a collar, and Alan gave her hands something else to do when he lifted her arms to his neck and dropped his mouth on hers.

He had to start with short, swift kisses because she was still out of breath. The rush of color in her cheeks delighted him. She was flustered, off guard. He'd very rarely caught Carroll flustered, and never off guard until recently.

"Alan, that doctor down there was seriously trying to offer you a job . . ."

"Mm-hmm." He nuzzled the lobe of her ear. So sweet.

"There were people down there, expecting to talk to you . . ."

"Yes." Her lashes were golden-tipped, fluttering around her cheeks. Her perfume suddenly surrounded him, faint and alluring, and his palm slipped to her bare throat at the V of her dress. Her heartbeat jumped under his hand.

"Alan, this is *crazy*. I don't know what you're doing."

"Sure you do," he murmured. "I'm necking." He added gently, "With you."

He soared down for some serious kiss-type ravishment. Leaning back against the wall for balance, he let his hands roam the silky material of her dress. Molding her closer to him, he felt her lips gradually yield under his, as soft and fragile as the petals of a rose. *Now, don't be too methodical for Godsake,* warned a small voice in his head.

But he just couldn't change all at once. His tongue methodically, thoroughly explored the inside of her mouth, not wanting to miss any possible cache of sweetness. She *was* sweet. And her skin reminded him of spring mornings; it was that fresh, that clear and soft. He'd wanted to tell her that for so long, but the words never seemed to leave his lips. With his touch, he tried to communicate what he'd failed to tell her in so many words.

Confusion rocked through Carroll. Earlier, in Alan's office and at the start of the conference, she'd been at ease, comfortable. Alan was just . . . Alan. She always knew where she stood with him. Now she wasn't absolutely certain she was standing at all. Around her was a silent corridor, a dim light, the smell of books, and the muted sound of laughter and conversation in the distance. Anyone could come up here. And those who did so would find some very harsh breathing, a woman not fighting a seduction very hard, and a man whose tongue was making delicious little snipes on the shell of her ear.

Shivers whispered through her. This just wasn't possible, not in the middle of a medical convention. Sex was a serious business, involving commitment and intimacy and worry that it would go well and that he wouldn't make fun of the dimple on her fanny. It wasn't the passionate abandonment she'd discovered in herself in a barn on a Saturday morning. And it certainly wasn't . . . well . . . just fun for its own sake.

Strange, but she seemed to be having an incredible

amount of fun. Of course, maybe she had an instant
case of flu that was making her nipples perky and all
the heat in her body settle in that one tiny spot. Or
maybe she was going crazy, because Alan's hand had
just discovered that her skirt parted like the Red Sea
and she was searching for his lips like a wanton
hussy who couldn't get enough. She heard his throaty
chuckle of approval, loved it.

Naughty was nice, a delicious discovery. Carroll
suddenly wanted to go home. There had been a lot of
good reasons why she'd postponed their sexual relationship, the main one being her unwillingness to
lead Alan on, since she wasn't sure she wanted marriage. At the moment, she didn't care about leading
him on, she didn't care about marriage, she didn't
care about relationships. For the first time, she was
absolutely sure everything was going to be right, and
all she wanted was for him to take her home to bed.

Alan had wanted little more than to take Carroll to
bed for months. His body calmly informed him that if
he waited much longer, he'd be better off signing up
for a class in torture. Inviting more torture, he slid
his hands to her bottom, urging her lower body to rub
where he was hurting most. His head dropped to her
shoulder. He planned to regain control any minute
now. The warmth of her cuddled against him, the
softness of her hair, and the sound of that sweet,
sweet hoarseness coming from her throat weren't
helping.

"Alan . . ."

"Hmmm?" She tried to move back; he wouldn't let
her. So he liked torture. So? He'd never guessed she
could be like this, so responsive, so vulnerable, so

. . . sensual. Or that, as a man, he could have made her feel that way.

"Have I told you how much I loved the roses?" she murmured in his ear.

He smiled, eyes still closed. "You've certainly been trying to convince me for several days that someone sent you roses."

Again, she tried to pull back, and this time he let her, just to see the sudden laughter in her eyes. Her lips were moist, her cheeks all high color. "They *were* sent anonymously," she said gravely.

"I'll kill him."

She laughed then, a private laugh not loud enough for anyone else to hear. "They were beautiful. They're still beautiful."

"Are they?"

"You know something?" She dropped her eyes to his collar, and started to straighten it. Her smile hovered, then vanished. "No one's ever given me roses," she said casually.

"The world's full of fools, then," he murmured. As he very obviously had been for a long time. If so little romancing made her so much more responsive, he was suddenly aware how badly he'd failed her before. And that there was endless sensual potential in this lady . . . if he could just convince his own body to be patient.

Unfortunately, his hormones were tired of all his patience, and were rioting within him, demanding release. A faint frown creased his brow, immediately erased when she looked up at him. "Ready to leave?"

Her eyes met his. "Yes." Surely he couldn't fail to understand what she was saying yes to?

She was just a little nervous as he started to drive. Something this good . . . she just didn't want the bubble to break. Outside there was a marvelous wind, chasing October's leaves from the trees, keening through the darkness. Clouds blocked and unblocked a view of the moon, as if they were playing a child's game of peekaboo.

She tensed again just slightly as they neared Alan's office. Her car was there and had to be picked up, but it wasn't a night she wanted to be separated from Alan, even for a minute, before they got home. Still, seconds later they passed the office, and her brows flickered up in surprise. "Did you forget my car?"

"For now."

Smiling, she curled up on the seat and relaxed. He felt as she did. Her eyelids fluttered sleepily down to half mast for the drive, and opened again only when the car stopped. Abruptly, her lips parted. Expecting to see her apartment, she saw dark woods weaving in moonlight and the dead end of a narrow road.

Alan switched off the engine, leaned back against his door, and smiled at her. "I've got an important question to ask you," he said softly.

Her heart thumped in triple time. "Yes?"

"I want to know all about you, Caro, and I was just realizing I don't know much about your childhood. Can you start with your earliest memory, and go on from there?"

Well, she'd always advocated getting to know each other, hadn't she? Biting back a sigh of frustration, Carroll began to tell Alan about her nursery school days.

* * *

Yawning, Carroll pushed open the classroom door and flicked on the light. Bleary eyed, she surveyed the purple unicorns dancing on the walls, the plush red rug in the center of the floor, and the box crammed with stuffed animals in the corner. There was no desk. As a speech therapist, she didn't believe in pushing a classroom atmosphere on the kids.

On this particular morning, the sandman had left a gritty feeling in Carroll's eyes, and the self-righteous corner of her brain was chiding her for arriving at work on half-power. Three hours of sleep just wasn't enough. Furthermore, she had the sneaky feeling that if she looked in a mirror, she'd see a fairly idiotic grin on her face.

Yawning again, she set down her container of orange juice and a paper bag that smelled suspiciously like doughnuts, then took off her coat. Beneath, she wore jeans and a white sweater with clowns embroidered on the front of it. She'd chosen to wear cloisonné dangling earrings that were shaped like little balloons in rainbow colors. Cathy loved balloons and lots of color, and Cathy was her first student this morning.

Blinking sleepily at the clock, she noted that she had, thank heaven, fifteen minutes before the child would arrive. She flopped down on the rug with the little girl's speech folder in her hand. The file absorbed her attention for a moment. Born with a hearing problem, Cathy had angelic blue eyes and a froth of blond curls. She was four. Five months ago, when her mother had first brought her in, Cathy had taken one look at Carroll and screamed bloody murder. The mother had been beside herself.

Carroll had not. Most kids hated speech therapy and with reason. A child who had failed to talk built up a fear of trying to speak, and that was exactly what Carroll had to ask her students to do—try. Risk failing. Fail. Try again, and again, and again. Speech was easy to teach. Building self-confidence in children with fragile egos was the tough job, and Carroll loved it.

But right now she couldn't keep her mind on Cathy for more than three seconds at a time. Alan's face kept intruding on her consciousness. She hadn't gotten home last night until after two, and then she'd gone home to a lonely bed. *Not* what she'd been expecting when they'd left the medical conference.

A wistful smile curved her lips. She still felt hung over from laughter. On a lover's lane, they'd shared embarrassing stories from when they were kids, critiqued nearly all the flavors on the Baskin Robbins' ice cream menu, shared other passions and peeves... heck, she didn't know what they'd talked about. They'd just talked and kept on talking.

Somewhere between 1:30 and 1:35 A.M., Carroll had come up with the amazing discovery that there was a tremendous difference between loving someone and being in love. She'd always loved Alan. Alan was easy to love. But last night she'd watched herself doing things that no sane person would do. Laughing at stories that couldn't possibly be funny to anyone else. Not caring that the hours were ticking by when she knew she had to work in the morning. Enjoying an awareness that her body was perpetually

turned on just from being in the same universe with
him . . .

She didn't have masses of sexual experience, but
she'd used the word *love* before and meant it. Still.
Something had always been missing—not loving,
not the ability to love, but that crazy, yearning, restless feeling of being *in* love.

A scrub brush probably couldn't wipe the silly
smile off her face. Helplessly, she yawned again and
tried to get serious. When a shadow darkened the
doorway, she looked up, prepared to see Cathy, and
instead saw the reason for her silly smile.

Alan looked wretched. There were pouches
beneath his eyes; the lines around them showed white
as they always did when he was overtired; and under
his jacket, he was wearing a shirt she'd never seen
before—a red shirt. Not his color. It didn't matter.
Six whole hours they'd been separated, far too long
in her current state of lunacy. She smiled. He smiled
back. "Hi," she said softly.

"Hi back."

Rather abruptly, she remembered that she was a
mature, rational woman and leaped to her feet.
"Alan, what on earth are you doing here?"

"Came to see you." He stifled an exhausted yawn,
and reached for the buttons of his jacket. "It occurred
to me last night how often you'd seen my office—
when I'd never seen where you work. I've wanted to
for weeks, Caro. And I was pretty sure you'd told me
you were always here on Tuesday, Wednesday, and
Friday mornings and that the school encouraged visi-
tors . . ."

"We do. We don't want the kids to feel isolated or different, and having lots of people around can help them feel less sensitive about their problems." She stopped abruptly; the subject couldn't be less relevant. "Alan, you must have had patients this morning."

"I did. One came very early; two canceled, and one was rescheduled for this afternoon." He tugged off his jacket, looked for a place to hang it. The only option appeared to be a child-size coat tree. His sleeves trailed on the floor. "You don't mind if I come in and watch you, do you?"

"No, of course not, but . . ." She saw her hands fluttering up, and stopped them. There was no reason to be flustered. She was delighted he was here, just surprised. "I'm afraid I haven't got a very exciting schedule this morning. If I'd known you wanted to come, I'd have asked you on a day when I had something more interesting. We've got some fantastic new testing equipment—"

"But then, I didn't come to see equipment. I came to see you." Since he certainly hadn't a prayer of sleeping the night before, he'd spent the wee hours of the morning alternately reading a book called *Love Foods for Successful Lovers* and making a list of ways to woo Carroll. One of the things on that list was coming here.

Watching her work hadn't exactly fit his list of heroic, exciting things a man should do for his woman, but it did have to do with love. Not just loving her, but proving it to her. He really was interested in her work and always had been, but the night before, it had occurred to him that he'd failed to *show* her his interest. "I promise not to get in your way."

"I wasn't worried about that."

He glanced around. "Where do you want me to sit?"

"Ummm." She gave him an apologetic glance. "On the floor, I'm afraid. Or I could bring in a chair for you . . ."

"I'll be just fine right here," he assured her, and settled cross-legged on the far corner of her red rug.

She looked at him uncertainly. "That isn't going to be comfortable."

"Sure it is."

"Are you positive? I mean . . ."

A little girl poked her head in the doorway; she was dressed in Oshkosh overalls and a fuzzy purple sweater. Alan's heart turned over, seeing the hearing aids in her ears. She wasn't much bigger than a minute, and she took one look at him and hurled herself at Carroll.

Carroll was prepared, arms ready to swing her up in a hug. There wasn't a sound for a few minutes, as the two carried on a rapid conversation in sign. Alan gathered very quickly that he was unwanted, that the child knew whatever was in the white bag on the shelf was a treat for her, and that she was in the habit of collecting a favorite stuffed animal from the corner before they started work.

He cleared his throat in embarrassment. In coming here, he'd wanted to show Carroll he cared about her work. It had stupidly never occurred to him that his presence might make her job more difficult.

"Doughnuts *after* speech," Carroll insisted finally. "Down we go, Cathy. Work time . . . but first I want you to meet Alan." The child pulled tighter on her arms. Carroll shot Alan a wink and smoothly rushed on, "Alan brought some orange juice just for you this morning, *and* some doughnuts. He's having problems with his *s*'s, and you're getting so good with them I thought you could help him."

The little girl looked suspiciously at Alan, who nodded gravely. Slowly, she consented to being slid out of Carroll's arms to the floor. She made another gesture in sign to Carroll, who firmly shook her head.

"From now on, we're going to communicate in speech."

Orange juice was served, spilled, cleaned up, and put aside. By then the blond urchin was batting her eyelashes at Alan and edging closer. Fifteen minutes later, the tyke was sitting on his lap, and they were both pretending they were snakes, making long hissing sounds.

"No, not quite," Carroll said gently. "Watch my mouth now. Watch my teeth. See how my teeth come together when I make the *s* sound?"

Alan watched her mouth. He watched her teeth. He made *s* sounds. Then *k* sounds. And then *d* sounds.

An hour later, Cathy was succeeded by Melissa, who had a lisp. At midmorning, Melissa was succeeded by Philip, a gangly six-year-old with a milk mustache, who had a tendency to stammer. Then there was Jimmy, who couldn't master the *l* sound.

At first, Alan was fascinated. Carroll was such a

pro. Nothing shook her. Melissa insisted on working
upside down—literally standing on her head. Philip
dissolved in tears. Carroll battled discouragement,
temper tantrums, fragile egos, and plain stubborn-
ness. She was the most beautiful battle-ax of a
teacher he'd ever come across, he thought lovingly.
Nothing deterred her from smoothly, gently prodding
the recalcitrant little ones into mastering their speech
lessons. At first amused that she'd made him part of
her class, he understood shortly thereafter that he'd
better toe the line. Helping the children came first.
He had no doubts that she'd make the President of
the United States sit down on the carpet and practice
consonants if he dared to darken the door.

After several hours, though, Alan's legs were
cramped, he'd earned two rainbow stickers on his
wrists, and the tedium of repetition was getting to
him. As lunchtime neared, he was dying. His right
leg had developed a charleyhorse. His jaw ached
from forming sounds. He'd had three cups of orange
juice spilled on him.

"Llllll," Caro repeated. "Make the tip of your
tongue touch the roof of your mouth, Jimmy. There
now, look at Alan. See how his tongue tickles the top
of his mouth?"

Alan obediently demonstrated by parting his lips
and making his tongue touch the roof of his mouth
for the fifteenth time. He was going to last the rest of
the morning. He *was*. He was interested in her work,
and he was going to prove it to her. In the meantime,
he tried to stretch his cramped leg. Jimmy, looking
for any excuse to be distracted, stopped working to
frown at him. Alan kept his leg exactly where it was,

and refrained from looking at his watch.

Finally, the boy left. Carroll bounced up from the carpet with a brilliant smile. "He did it, didn't he?" she crowed. "He came in here believing he'd never master that sound!"

"*You* did it," Alan corrected.

She waved her hand dismissively. "*He* did," she insisted, and stood there gloating so hard he wanted to kiss her.

"Who's next?" he asked instead.

"No one—lunchtime."

"Darn." He shook his head and slowly, carefully, straightened his legs so he could stand up without pain. Blood cascaded to his feet in an icy waterfall of feeling.

"You really enjoyed it, Alan? You weren't bored?" Her eyes danced with both eagerness and sudden anxiety.

"Bored, are you kidding? I just can't believe how fast the morning went. Only wish I could stay for the afternoon session." The fibs rolled glibly from his tongue. Who cared? He couldn't stop looking at her. Caro was glowing, within, without, all over.

"I know you can't. You've got appointments; I never expected you to spare this much time." She sprinted over to him and surged up on tiptoe for a kiss. "Thank you for coming," she said softly.

She tasted like orange juice, sticky fingers, and Caro. She'd also rarely been the first one to offer a kiss. "Dinner tomorrow." He kissed her nose. "My place." He kissed her chin. "Pick you up at seven?"

"I'll be ready."

Outside, Alan hauled fresh air into his lungs and

turned his face up toward the sunlight. Then he strode to his car with a step that was uncontrollably cocky, cramped muscles or no cramped muscles. It was working. He was going to win her. He was even beginning to enjoy turning himself inside out to do it. And if Caro liked surprises, he had a few more up his sleeve.

He was determined to grow old beside that woman, and just as determined to make her happy.

Chapter 5

AT SEVEN-THIRTY the next evening, Carroll stepped ahead of Alan into his apartment. "You still didn't say who was cooking tonight . . . as if I didn't know," she said teasingly.

"So you *think* you know. As it happens, the kitchen is completely off limits to you tonight." Alan hung up both their coats, casting a critical eye on his living room.

Everything was set up as planned, but he couldn't shake the feeling that it just wasn't enough. The picnic lunch, the roses, necking in a deserted hallway— they'd worked. Carroll was blossoming in front of his eyes. Unfortunately, the small successes had made him see that huge ones might be possible if he could just manage this business of courting her properly. If he was man enough. If he could completely change, *be* a different kind of man for her . . .

He caught her soft spaniel-brown eyes on him, banished his lingering worries, and grinned. "I see that look in your eyes, but you're dead wrong, kitten," he said lazily. "I not only cooked dinner, but it's ready and waiting for us."

Dropping her purse on an end table, she raised a skeptical eyebrow. "I see. You've hired a catering service," she said blandly.

"No."

"Your mother came over earlier to put something in the oven while you were picking me up?"

"No."

"Good Lord. You've kidnapped some poor woman, and you have her tied to the stove?"

"*No.*" He planted a kiss on the tip of her nose, a delectable nose that was just a little pink from the cold outside. Her lips were equally tempting, and if her eyes didn't stop reflecting shy invitations, he was going to be completely diverted from his higher purpose. Dammit, a true hero should be able to get his mind off making love to her for at least two minutes at a time. A true hero would successfully whet his lover's sensual appetite until her need was beyond control and her desire reached a fever pitch... exactly what he wanted to do.

Exactly what he was *going* to do if it killed him. Teasingly, he patted her fanny. "You can stop looking so sassy. I've discovered over the last two weeks that any man can learn to cook."

"I'm terribly sorry for doubting you," Carroll said gravely, and resigned herself to a burned dinner. Alan was a whiz at making toast. To give him full credit, he wasn't bad at ordering a pizza or bringing in Chinese food, either.

It hardly mattered, when dinner was the last thing on her mind. Alan was wearing black, a pirate-style shirt she'd never seen before. She was becoming used to the new and unexpected additions to his wardrobe; reading the new sensual look in his eyes was something else. One minute they were laughing and talking the way they always had; the next she felt lavishly, mysteriously studied by those rich blue eyes of his. It was enough to make a sensible woman's toes tingle.

Weeks before, she would have scoffed at the thought. These days she was inclined to sweep a lot of issues under the rug because of those toes, yet her feelings weren't frivolous but fragile. His continued attentions made her feel loved as she'd never imagined feeling loved. She wasn't so egotistical as to think she was as fascinating, beautiful, and scintillating as Alan's eyes kept assuring her she was, but inside she felt newly rich, as though every nerve ending now had a coating of luster.

"Now just relax, kick off your shoes, and prepare for a feast," Alan called over his shoulder. "You're not allowed in the kitchen—I'll bring you a glass of tequila."

"Tequila?" They both liked a can of beer during a football game and an occasional glass of wine with dinner. Tequila, never. "Alan, you haven't been experimenting with any fancy Mexican sauces, have you?" she asked with alarm.

Alan was bringing her a frosted glass of tequila with a layer of salt on the rim. "*Will* you sit down and trust me?" he scolded before disappearing into the kitchen again. "It's *not* refried beans," he called back by way of reassurance.

Hmmm. Still standing, Carroll took a sip from the glass, shuddered, and stared at the misleadingly innocuous clear liquid. It was pure and simple firewater . . . and it left a faint dusting of salt on her upper lip.

Maybe it was the sting of the tequila, but her eyes

abruptly started playing tricks on her. Alan's apartment was normally as familiar as her own. A bay window looked onto a courtyard; his walls were cream-colored stucco; and his traditional furniture in brown and cream reflected comfort and neatness— except for the bookshelf crammed with medical journals.

Carroll took another sip of the tequila, and let her tongue make a delicate swipe at the salt residue on her lip. The room hadn't drastically changed, but her eyes were drawn with startling speed to the huge new oil painting that hung over his couch. As she studied the picture, the impressionistic blur of siennas and golds and flesh tones gradually settled into the shapes of a naked man and woman. And the longer she stared at it, the more obvious it became that the man and woman weren't playing tiddlywinks.

Heavens. Her gaze swiftly took in the rest of the room. All clutter had disappeared. His medical books and journals had been neatly put away. The only printed material left casually out was an expensive book of prints bound in hand-tooled leather. Orientals prints. Erotic Oriental prints. Alan never looked at that kind of thing.

Or maybe he did.

Absently, she rubbed a finger on her temple. Over the past two weeks, she realized that she'd been unfair ever to peg Alan into a predictable slot. And there was no question that she relished the discovery of dimensions in him—and in herself—she hadn't known about before, but occasionally she felt . . . well . . . lost. She never knew what he was going to do next, and just a little of that old predictability would have been nice to hold on to. Not that he wasn't entitled to buy an oil or look at sultry nudes if he wanted to.

And maybe he'd suddenly developed a liking for pillows, because there were two huge rust-colored velvet ones on the floor. Put together, they were almost large enough to make a mattress. And next to them was a black onyx tray with three candles on it.

Carroll's eyes narrowed on the ripples of wax and charred wicks of the candles. They'd clearly been used. If Alan had been anyone but Alan, she might have immediately jumped to the suspicious conclusion that used candles and floor pillows and a suggestive painting on the wall added up to another woman in his life. She did not come to that conclusion; she simply took another rapid sip of tequila. She trusted Alan. Totally.

"You've been making a few changes around here," she called out conversationally.

"A few. An old friend did the painting. Like it?"

As long as his old friend was a man, she liked it just fine. "Colorful," she murmured dryly.

"Didn't hear you?"

"Very nice," she called back. "Is your artist friend anyone I know?"

He smiled by way of answer as he carried in a large tray from the kitchen. "You haven't been making yourself comfortable," he chided. "This is a shoes-off kind of dinner. I told you."

"Yes." She studied the tray as she obediently slipped off her shoes, well aware Alan was lighting the three candles and switching out the other lights. The tequila suddenly settled in her stomach with a tattoo of Hello there, Nerves.

So this was finally the night? But then, she'd known it was, and she wanted it to be; that was why she was wearing brand-new French panties and a violet bra under her sweater and slacks, why she'd bathed in perfumed water. And if she'd had any doubts that Alan was in the mood, he'd dispelled them with the kiss when he'd picked her up. That kiss was from a man who was tired of waiting.

She'd responded like a woman who was tired of making him wait, but the tray in his hands was almost as diverting as the nude oil on the wall. "Alan, what is this?" Following his lead, she settled on the carpet with one of the huge pillows behind her.

"Tapas. They call them 'the small foods of Spain.' You're going to love these, Caro." He pointed to each small plate on the tray, identifying the delicacies. "Quail with a thyme sauce. Rolled anchovy fillets on picks. Poached squid in a hot tomato sauce. Wild mushrooms, raw oysters, and cactus paddles."

"Sounds wonderful." She gave him a brilliant smile, her heart sinking. He'd gone to so much trouble. Every dish had been artfully arranged, all for her, but she didn't have the fortitude to swallow an anchovy. As for the rest . . .

"Thought it would be more fun to picnic on the carpet. Wait until you taste, kitten."

She was more than willing to wait, but he nudged a tidbit toward her lips. She clamped down, chewed delicately, and reached quickly for the tequila, trying not to make the move appear violent or desperate. "That must be the squid?"

He nodded. "I figured I'd experiment with one kind of foreign food a week. For next week, I found an entire cookbook full of recipes from Tibet; they call for spices I'd never even heard of. Anyway, Spanish tonight. Like it?"

"Mmmm." To get her mind off the squid, she motioned to the pillows. "I should have some pillows like these in the classroom. The kids would love them. I don't know if I told you about this little Miranda I've been working with, but—"

"Carroll?"

"Hmm?" She looked up, smiling.

"No," he said, gently but firmly. "Another time I'll hear about her, sweet. But tonight we're not going to talk about kids or work or anything . . . except us." He watched her lips form a delicate O as the faintest color warmed her flesh. "That sweater looks lovely on you, Caro."

"This old thing?" The black sweater was new, cashmere with a low cowl neckline. The off-white wool slacks were also new, and the outfit was marvelously flattering to her figure. Misleadingly so, as she was only now beginning to realize. When she took off her clothes later, he'd find out exactly what needed to be hidden and what didn't. She should have worn a sack.

In the meantime, her heart refused to stop thumping in her chest. Hiding behind half-lowered lashes, she found she couldn't take her eyes off Alan. Candlelight played on his strong features, glowed on his beard, added a flame and mystery to his eyes. He was a gentle man, but these last two weeks she'd had delicious, frightening, exciting, enticing glimpses of the passionate lover he could be. And because of him, she was just beginning to understand that she was much more sensual than she'd ever believed. *Please, Alan, couldn't we completely forget about dinner and just . . .*

He leaned toward her. Her breath stopped altogether. "You've got to try the cactus paddles," he urged.

"The . . . oh. I will, I will." Her eyes dropped to the small plate he'd just filled for her.

"I had to look pretty far and wide for something I knew you'd never tried before."

"You didn't have to do that," she said softly, and entirely truthfully. By that time, she'd had a taste. "Really different," she equivocated between gulps of tequila. Well? You didn't cut a man down who'd spent an afternoon in the kitchen just to please you.

He refilled her glass, and then leaned forward to brush the bits of salt from her upper lip. His thumb lingered, loving the texture of her mouth. That slight touch made her tremble, almost imperceptibly. It made every ghastly hour between sink and oven that afternoon worth it.

His mind groped frantically for something else. The dinner was going fine, but unfortunately it was just a dinner. Any man could have made her a romantic dinner. There had to be something more he could do, some completely new experience he could offer Caro . . .

"Alan?"

"Hmmm?"

"Would I know the name of the artist who did your painting?"

He shook his head. "I doubt it. Her name's Jennifer Spencer."

The mushrooms were close to edible, but suddenly wouldn't go down. "You know her well?" Carroll asked casually.

"Used to." He considered capturing Caro's expression on film, but didn't have a camera handy. Her smile would have cut butter, but her eyes were sparklers. Jealousy, he thought contentedly. Rusty wheels turned in his head. "Old lovers—we all have them, don't we, Caro?"

"Yes, of course, we do." Which she abruptly discovered was fine for her, but not at all for him. Who *was* the witch? Carroll glanced again at the painting, then flashed a demure smile at Alan. That oil was going to liven up a garage sale someday soon. "Did you know her long?"

"Hmmm." He leaned back and switched the stereo on low. The speakers in the far corner moaned the faint sound of a rushing surf, as if the ocean were just out of reach in the dark room, hearable, smellable, tastable. Other men had undoubtedly played her plain old music. "Remember the first boy you went out with?" he asked idly.

Since it was obvious she was no longer hungry, Alan pushed aside the tray, readjusted the pillows, and drew Caro closer. She tucked her head willingly in the curve of his shoulder, her face lifted to his. She was waiting for him to kiss her, he could feel it. The pulse in her throat had a life of its own.

He touched that pulse with a fingertip, felt a fierce answering chord of desire from deep inside him, and fought to control it. It would be so easy to make love to her now, but it was more than willingness he wanted from Caro, and for Caro. "Your first date?" he coaxed again.

"Mmmm . . . a boy named Kirk Polansky," she said absently, barely aware of what she was saying. The candles and the dark room and the mystical ocean sounds and Alan's hand, so gently fingering through her hair . . . her bloodstream announced that she was being set up. If any other man had tried it, she would have handed him his walking papers, but this was Alan. She loved being set up by Alan. Every nerve ending was increasingly ticklish with anticipation.

"Tell me about it, Caro."

"About my first date?" She shook her head, chuckling up at him. "A terrible story, Alan. We went to a homecoming dance; his mother had to drive us. He had braces, five left feet, and kissed me at the door like a fish, lips all puckered up, eyes closed." Humor sparkled in her eyes. "Which isn't to cut him down, poor boy. At fifteen, I had braces and five left feet, too."

He smoothed her hair back, his fingers idly playing with the strands. "But you didn't kiss like a fish."

"I may have."

"You didn't," he assured her. "How about the second boy you went out with?"

"Don't really remember," Carroll admitted. "The next one I remember was . . ." She hesitated. Why were they talking about this? And the tequila must have gone straight to her head, because she hadn't thought about such things in years.

"Tell me," Alan encouraged.

"Oh . . . a boy named Mark."

"And you were how old?"

"Sixteen or so."

"First love?"

She flushed. "No, it was nothing like that." Her fingers splayed on the silk folds of his shirt. Beneath, she could feel the warmth of Alan's chest, the solidity of muscle, the comfort of his heartbeat. There was nothing she couldn't tell Alan. "In high school, the boys called me 'the challenge' behind my back," she said dryly. "It seems I built up a reputation for being a Goody Two-shoes. Anyway, Mark was tall and good-looking and strictly bad news—no decent girl in school would date him. Everyone knew he only wanted one thing." Carroll chuckled, offering Alan a mischievous smile. "In short, he was the best chance I ever had to get into trouble and I blew it."

Not from where Alan was sitting. "I take it you didn't go out with him?"

"Oh, yes, I did. I even knew the football team had made bets on whether or not he would score. Darn it, that was partly why I accepted the date." Carroll idly ran a hand through her hair, remembering. "Alan, you probably can't understand this . . ."

"Hey. Give me a try," he coaxed lightly. Surely, she wasn't afraid he would judge or criticize her? He would never do that. He did wonder fleetingly if the bastard was still alive.

"Well . . ." She laughed, a little nervously. "You know how you are when you're sixteen? You think nothing can hurt you, you're sure the whole world is out there waiting for you to explore it, and you want to try everything at least once. I was so tired of that ice-maiden label, Alan, and maybe I just wanted to see what I was missing. I had big visions of a wild date. Maybe doing things I'd always wanted to do, like staying up until dawn, like climbing the sandstone mountains at Shades Park by moonlight, like canoeing on the Wabash at midnight."

Alan mentally stored those tidbits. "So what happened?" he encouraged.

"He took me to a drive-in movie and spilled popcorn all over me," Carroll said dryly. "Somehow that got us laughing. I think that spoiled his whole image as the football-team stud. I didn't even get a kiss at the door, no pass, nothing, but believe it or not, we had a terrific time. A few days later, he even punched some guy who dared to ask how he'd made out with me. Darn it, the guy acted like my big brother for almost a year."

"Did he?" Amused now, Alan discovered an eyelash that had fallen on her cheek, a tiny black crescent of silk against cream-soft skin. He brushed it away with the pad of his thumb and then leaned back, studying her. His eyes turned thoughtful. "So . . . you were stuck with being a 'good girl' a little longer."

"Yup."

"No other chances to stay up until dawn?"

"Plenty in college, when I used to study all night. Seeing the dawn that way just isn't all it's cracked up to be."

"No," he agreed absently. For that matter, climbing around the sandstone hills in Shades State Park by moonlight struck him as a good way to get killed. Which left him only the last of her fantasies to act on.

Regretfully, his gaze wandered over her slim form, over the soft slope of her breasts draped in black cashmere to the curve of her hips in white. Caro wasn't tipsy, but she was definitely relaxed. He allowed himself one long moment of imagining her body without the black and white garments, all supple and lithe and willing and bare, then abruptly surged to his feet and reached down for her hand. "Up," he urged.

"What?"

He switched on a lamp, bent over to blow out the candles, and reached for her hand again. "I think it's time you canoed on the Wabash at midnight."

Her lips parted in surprise. "Alan, I was just talking. It was just a sixteen-year-old's fantasy, for heaven's sake! We don't have to—"

"I'm afraid we do," he announced firmly, and hoped she didn't hear the regret in his voice. Possibly the last thing on earth he wanted to do was head out into a cold night in a canoe, but that wasn't the point. Doing something absolutely special for Caro was the point. Tequila might have loosened the forgotten fantasy from her tongue, but a bulldozer couldn't have stopped Alan from following through with it.

"You can't be serious," Carroll said incredulously.

He was already heading for the telephone. It wasn't going to be all that easy to find a canoe livery open after dark in late October. "Think you can manage to fit into a pair of my old jeans for a few hours?"

* * *

The old codger waved them off from the river-bank. "Now, don't worry about a thing, you two. Just remember, now, three miles down the river you'll see the blue light—a big thing, no way you'll miss it. I'll be gone on home, mind you, but you just tie the canoe up secure when you're done, and the gate'll be open so you can get your car out."

"Thank you again for everything," Carroll called after him. A moment later, he was out of sight and she leaned comfortably back against Alan. "Nice old man, wasn't he? Not many people would have been willing to go to such trouble for strangers."

Privately, Alan saw the codger a little differently, but then, privately he'd slipped the man a few bills, each one emblazoned with Ben Franklin's face. The old guy's shrewd eyes had lit up like Christmas lights. As he'd driven them to the landing, he'd repeated again and again that the two of them could use his canoes any time, any season, and any hour of the day or night.

It didn't matter. Sitting straight, Alan dipped the paddle into the smooth, quiet waters of the river. Carroll was half sitting and half reclining on a cushion, cradled between his legs, her head against his stomach. When she tilted her face up, she was smiling. "I'm afraid he thought we were nuts, Alan."

"Probably." He added teasingly, "One of us *does* look like a vagrant."

"What's this? You don't like my outfit?" His jeans fit her just about as well as his corduroy jacket, and his old tennies stayed on her feet only because she had put on three pairs of socks. She could hardly have worn the outfit she'd had on at dinner for this venture, and to drive to her place for other clothes would have wasted time.

"I love your outfit," he assured her.

Which was odd, Carroll thought. He looked at her as if black cashmere sweaters couldn't begin to compete with oversized jackets and baggy jeans. Really, it was a very strange sensation, to be in love with a man who had such serious vision problems.

And she was so in love with him. Initially, she'd hated the thought of disrupting their evening, and couldn't believe he was serious. But Alan had made it clear he loved the idea; they'd laughed so much on the way here; and darn it, it *was* something she'd always wanted to do. More than that, who else could she have done this with but Alan?

The Wabash could be a murky gray-green by daylight. At night, the river was black and smooth and mysterious. Steam whispered off the surface in wispy puffs, and the steep banks were shrouded in brush and trees.

On a very rare occasion, nature could forget about bringing on winter and freezing temperatures and threatening clouds and do something incredibly special with a night in October. This was one of those nights. The stars were low and clear and bright, thousands of them winking against an ebony sky. She could smell the trees, the water, the night itself. The air was almost warm, and the faintest breeze whispered in her hair.

The lights of Lafayette sparkled above them on both sides. Traffic sounds and even voices carried on

the river. Civilization was right there, so close, yet
they were totally alone, cocooned in silky darkness.
The only sound she clearly heard was the steady,
rhythmic dip of the paddle.

A half-hour must have passed before Alan lifted
the paddle and simply let them drift downstream.
One never took a current on a river for granted; Alan
knew that from the hours he'd spent in a canoe as a
kid, but for a few moments there could be no possible danger. "Is this what you had in mind when you
were sixteen?" he murmured.

She tilted her head back to look at him. "A thousand times better. Isn't it special, Alan?"

"Very." But it was Carroll he was staring at. Her
face was glowing by moonlight, and her eyes were
magic. "Next time, don't save up those dreams," he
chided her teasingly. "Bring them out of hiding so we
can do something about them."

"I felt silly," she admitted.

"For confessing to dreams?"

"I always thought you would laugh."

"Never, Caro." He couldn't wait any longer to
drop a kiss on her mouth.

The kiss was upside down, making them both
smile just before lips touched lips. Shortly after that,
she decided she could get very used to upside-down
kisses . . . but she didn't have to. Careful not to dis-
turb the balance of the canoe, he turned her and lifted
her a few inches so her head was on a level with his
shoulder. That way her eyes could meet his, and his
arm could move where it belonged, around her, and
his mouth . . .

His mouth wooed and beguiled and tempted her, teaching her all sorts of new dimensions in the oldest of arts. There were follow-me sorcerer's kisses and confectioner's sugar kisses and lazy, slow, languid kisses. *We have forever,* his lips promised her. She saw stars, the craziest glow of blue light, the loving shine of his eyes.

Inexorably, the river flowed beneath them; they paid no attention. The flow and movement became part of them; Alan's husky murmur seemed part of the mist, her answering laughter a blend with the moonlight. In time, they stopped, and Carroll simply lay in his arms, eyes closed.

Alan took up the paddle again. "We should reach the landing soon," he said regretfully.

Her eyes blinked uneasily back open. "Alan?"

"Hmmm?"

"Do you think there's any chance we passed that blue light the man told us about?"

"Honey—did you see it?"

"I . . ." It was a little tough to explain that she'd gotten blue lights and stars and loving confused for a short time.

Abruptly, Alan turned the paddle to slow the canoe. "When?" he said briskly.

"Back . . . umm . . . when neither of us was paying too much attention."

Smoothly, swiftly, Alan turned the canoe around, shipped the paddle, and unzipped his jacket. Traveling upstream was a little harder than traveling down. "Now, don't get nervous," he said soothingly. "It can't be that far. We'll find it."

"I'm not nervous," Carroll assured him.

"There's nothing to worry about."

"I'm not worried."

"It just might take us a little longer to get home than we expected, that's all."

He dropped her off at home at three in the morning. Carroll was so tired she could barely manage to strip off her clothes and climb into bed. But when she did so, and when she closed her eyes in those last moments before sleep, she was still smiling.

Canoeing against the current hadn't exactly been fun, and the old codger's blue light was the faintest wink of color between trees, almost impossible to find. Still, that wasn't what had mattered to Carroll. They'd laughed through all of it; they'd shared; the whole night had been delicious for her. And what the heck, it was downright exhilarating to know that her kisses had actually made Alan forget where they were.

Alan, driving home, was miserable. Some hero he'd turned out to be.

He'd blown the whole romantic adventure, and it was one he should have easily been able to pull off. He knew canoes. He knew better than to ignore landmarks; he shouldn't have let their location slip from his mind for even an instant.

That wasn't the whole problem, though. From cooking romantic dinners to setting up candlelight seductions to canoeing at midnight, he'd had high hopes of tricking Carroll into believing he had a little honest-to-goodness swashbuckler in his blood.

The problem was just that. Tricks. He didn't want to trick her into believing he was what she wanted and needed in a man. He wanted to be that man.

Chapter 6

CARROLL USUALLY ENJOYED a Monday night visit with her family, but the kids had been horrendous all day, an icy rain had made the drive treacherous, and her car was making ominous noises as though it wanted a new muffler. By the time she pushed open the back door to her mother's kitchen, it was seven in the evening, and little devils were pounding in her head.

"Anybody home?" She peeked in.

"Caro, you're going to have to talk with your sister!"

Maud was feeding plates to the dishwasher at a clattering rate. The teapot was whistling all by its lonesome on the stove, totally ignored. Not taking her eyes off her mother, Carroll shrugged out of her jacket and rescued the teapot.

Maud was dressed in a paisley blouse and camel skirt and the sling pumps she'd worn to work that day. She looked trim, whirlwind efficient, far too attractive to be the mother of two grown daughters, and at the moment ready to climb the nearest wall. "We've run into a few more snags in the wedding plans?" Carroll asked sympathetically.

"It is *not* possible to put on this wedding with only two more weeks to prepare for it, and that's that!

Would you *please* go talk to your sister?"

"Sure, Mom," Carroll said soothingly.

Nancy was in the living room. An absolutely exquisite white satin wedding gown was draped over the couch, a photograph album was open on the floor, and four sample books from florists littered the tables. Dressed in a neon-yellow shirt with skintight black pants, Nancy was barefoot and pacing. The minute she saw Carroll, she stopped. "Thank heavens you're here. You've got to talk to mother, Caro. She's being totally impossible!"

"All right."

"You're the only one who could ever make her see sense."

"Hmm," Carroll said amiably, and wandered out of the living room toward the closed door of the den. She knocked once, then poked her head in. The TV was blaring the news; her dad had his feet up on his recliner with a pipe in one hand and the newspaper in the other. "Safe to come in here?" she asked.

David chuckled and raised his eyes to the ceiling. "I'm trying my best to stay out of harm's way. Come in and give us a kiss. You look like a breath of sanity."

"I am," she said mischievously. No point in telling her dad she felt like bursting into tears. She bent to kiss his soft cheek. "Can you fill me in before I go back out there and face the lions?"

"They're both totally irrational," David Laker said simply.

"I could see that."

"And over nothing. We've got the church, the

hall, and the dress. What more does anybody need to get married?"

"A blood test."

David looked alarmed. "Lord, don't mention that. It'll be just one more detail they'll find to argue over."

"Hmmm." Carroll kissed him again, mostly because he deserved a reward for surviving in such an argumentative household over the years, and headed back for the door. "Come out and save me if you hear the sound of things being thrown."

"I've already heard the sound of things being thrown. That was when I ducked in here. You can handle them, Caro. You always have."

Chuckling, Caro wandered back out, mentally told the demons in her head to stop pounding, and rearranged her face into suitable smpathetic lines before reappearing in the living room doorway. Nance by that time had flung herself into a chair, and raised her head only long enough to give Carroll a dramatic look, full of pathos and despair.

"Do you see what I mean? She's completely unreasonable."

"Haven't talked to Mom yet. Why don't you tell me what's wrong first?"

"Everything's wrong. Everything. The caterer backed out with only two weeks to go before the wedding—"

"Don't worry. I'll find another caterer. What else?" Bending down, Carroll carefully lifted the gorgeous wedding dress and hung it in the hall closet.

"The veil. Mother wants me to wear her veil, and

I don't want to hurt her feelings, but it's old-fashioned."

"So it's old-fashioned. Weddings are supposed to be old-fashioned. Besides, we both know you're not going to hurt Mom's feelings, so you wear the veil and love it. What else?"

"Caro—"

"What else?"

"Flowers," Nance said glumly. "I want to carry a single rose, and mother wants me to carry a traditional bouquet. Look—"

"I don't have to look," Carroll said patiently, and bent down to start closing floral sample books. "You want to carry a single rose; you carry a single rose. Now what?"

Photographers, decorating the hall, ordering the wedding cake, what kind of wedding cake, liquor or just wine for the wedding reception... "If only Stéphane were here," Nancy wailed. "It just can't all be done in two weeks. There's no way."

There was, of course, always a way. Nancy was reasonably calm by the time Maud marched into the room. A short time later, the three women were dissolved in laughter, the arguments forgotten. Spats had always been fierce between her volatile mother and sister, but they'd never lasted long, particularly when Carroll was there to play diplomat.

Though she loved her family, Carroll no longer felt up to playing diplomat, and knelt at the hearth to start a fire. She had been freezing all day. The little flames licking at the kindling felt good. Not warm enough, but good. Better yet would be to curl up on the couch next to Alan, her head in the crook of his shoulder, his arm around her waist, and her increasingly miserable body safe, snug, and sheltered.

Better yet would be to marry the man. Unfortunately, the steady patter about weddings made her starkly aware that Alan hadn't mentioned marriage in some time now. Or houses. Or children.

Just love.

Her smile came from nowhere . . . or maybe from the delivery of orchids earlier in the day. Anonymous, of course. And someone—some crazy stranger—had left a package on the front seat of her car the day before that. The package was huge, just as huge as the white velvet unicorn inside it. The frivolity of the giant stuffed animal touched her far more than the flowers. When she'd called to thank Alan, he'd denied everything, with a lot of throat clearing that made her smile.

Still, she firmly banished the image of Alan from her mind. Later. She certainly didn't want to see him when her complexion looked like white mud and her body was begging her to retire from the human race.

"Well, I'm going to join David and let you two girls talk," Maud announced. "Want me to make some hot cocoa first?"

"No, thanks, Mom," Carroll said.

"It's a better night for apricot brandy."

Carroll winced, but Nancy had already bounced up. She brought a decanter and two glasses back from the kitchen, and poured brandy for both of them. "Everything fine with Alan?"

"Great." Carroll looked at the orange liquid in the glass Nancy handed to her, then simply set it down.

"You two do anything special on Saturday night?"

"Yes," Carroll said, and sneezed. "Believe it or not, after dinner we went canoeing on the river."

"You *what?* Your Alan?" Nancy pivoted, took a very good look at Carroll, and frowned. "You look terrible."

"Thanks."

"You're not getting sick on us, are you, Caro?"

"I never get sick," Carroll reminded her.

"Because we're never going to get through this wedding if you come down with something." Nancy's tone rose in increasing alarm. "After two years in Quebec, I'd forgotten how Mom and I fight when we're in the same house for longer than forty-eight hours. You can't get sick."

"I'm not, I'm not." She sat up and tried to look perky. "Come on, let's talk about the wedding."

Nancy shook her head. "We've been talking about the wedding all day, every day for two weeks. Let's talk about your Saturday night date. Better yet, let's talk about *your* wedding."

"He hasn't asked."

"A detail." Nancy dismissively waved that aside with a gesture of her hand. "The important thing is whether you're sure you want to spend the rest of your life with him."

"I'm sure," Carroll said quietly. The room was vaguely spinning, reminding her that weeks ago that was exactly what she'd been worried about, that Alan never made her head spin. He did now. Regularly. Being in love wasn't unlike having the flu, one minute dizzy-headed, one minute traumatized by despair . . . in so many ways, Alan bewildered her lately.

He'd changed, and rationally she kept trying to convince herself she should be worried about the reason for those changes. The Fiero made no sense; Alan needed a practical car. She wasn't all that happy with the idea of living in a barn; his beard left a chafing rash in embarrassing places; squid was never going to be her favorite food. She had no idea what he was going to do next.

Emotionally, though, she didn't need to know what he was going to do next. Who really cared if the man took up gourmet cooking? He had prepared the dinner especially for her, and that was the point. Affection, respect, and trust had always been part of their relationship. The last two weeks, in really talking together, doing all these different things together, those feelings had simply intensified, and love and the strongest of desires had been added to them.

He loved her. Everything he'd done had shown her that. At core, Alan had her heart and, if he ever got around to taking it, her body. A whimsical smile curved her lips. "I'm going to marry that man," she said firmly.

"Good."

Heavens, she felt strange. The room really *was* spinning. "I'm going to marry a man who thinks I love stuffed animals, who serves me cactus paddles for dinner, and who wants to live in a barn," Carroll said vaguely.

There was a moment's silence before Nancy bounced up from her chair and came over to feel her forehead. "I thought so. You've got a fever."

"He chased me around a medical conference. I

don't know if you can understand the monumental difficulties involved in chasing anyone around a medical conference . . ."

"I'm getting you an aspirin. Immediately."

"He sat there for three hours, bored absolutely stiff, and practiced all those *s*'s and *l*'s."

"Skip the aspirin. I'm calling Mother," Nancy said firmly.

"Don't go," warbled the frail voice. The five-year-old was little more than two dark burning eyes surrounded by white—white sheets, white blankets, and white walls in the background.

"Sweetheart, I promised you I'd stay until you fell asleep, and I will." Alan glanced at the clock on the hospital room wall. It was Monday night and nearing midnight, something his limbs and eyes and head could have already told him. Around nine, weariness had settled over him like a pall, but he still hadn't been able to leave the hospital.

Right after visiting hours were over and her mother had left, Susie had changed her mind about having her adenoids out in the morning. She'd decided definitely not to.

"One more story," she coaxed now.

Three stories later, Alan was finally free to tug on his coat and escape the hospital. A still night and a sky full of stars greeted him outside. His car was the only one left in its row. As he started the engine, he told himself for the hundredth time that these late-night hospital visits were unnecessary. During the day, he always checked on the few pediatrics patients he had scheduled for minor surgery.

His problem, as he'd mentally told himself a dozen times, was that he didn't have pediatrics patients; he had Susie and Johnny and Billy and Kim. For a short time, they weren't their parents' kids but his. An attitude that his mentors had tried very hard to purge him of in medical school—with absolutely no success.

At home, he shucked his clothes and stood for long minutes under a hot shower, which against all odds woke him up.

Lying in the darkness, fully awake, he stared at the ceiling and thought of Carroll. Sleeping alone was not fun. Sleeping alone was even less fun when a man knew there was a woman on the other side of the city who was more than willing to share her bed with him. Not at this hour, of course. He glanced at the luminous face of his clock radio. Two A.M. No, hardly at this hour, but the principle was the same.

He'd spent two nights trying to think of some way to ensure that making love with him would be the most unforgettable experience of Caro's life. It appeared he was going to spend a third night the same way.

The thing is, he lacked daring. Imagination. A true spirit of romantic devilment. Women wanted things like that. A true romantic hero would not think about the time or worry about interrupting her sleep. A true romantic hero took chances. He thought up much more exciting things than roses and gourmet dinners. He took his lady completely by surprise.

Abruptly, Alan sat up in bed and switched on the light. The mirror over his dresser reflected back a squinting man with disheveled hair, gray pajama tops, and a determined scowl. *You're crazy,* said a little voice in his head. *You can't do that. Go back to bed.*

Clean black socks were neatly folded in his drawer. He put those on after he'd pulled on a dark sweater and jeans. Yawning, he grabbed a jacket and stuffed his keys in his back pocket. *She'll have the little men come to put you away. They'll be smiling patiently and carrying a straitjacket . . .*

He mentally suggested an anatomically impossible feat to his little voice, and persevered. A man had to do what a man had to do. Maybe the canoe trip had been a bomb, but he could make this work. Caro wouldn't laugh at him. And if she took it in the right spirit, neither of them would be sleeping alone after this. Ever.

He refused to feel another qualm, until he reached Carroll's building, parked the car, and took a long look at the dark windows of her apartment. She *was* unquestionably asleep.

Sleepy, however, could be an advantage. She wouldn't be quite so likely to think he'd lost his mind. *Stop that kind of negative thinking,* he commanded himself. Climbing out of the car, he took firm steps around the side of her building.

He knew which windows went to her bedroom. The trick was getting to them. He pivoted around to make sure no patrol cars were anywhere in sight, then let his eyes focus on the oak tree in her courtyard. No one could have asked for a sturdier tree, and there was a thick branch right next to her window. The trunk, however, grew six feet straight up before he could conceivably get a foothold. *If* he meant to climb the tree.

I think, the little voice said patiently, *this has gone far enough. Go home, Alan.*

Actually, the spirit of it was beginning to get to him. He wanted Caro. He wanted Caro with every breath he took these days. He breathed, dreamed, and thrived on wanting her—it was not just a sexual need but a driving force that colored every hour in each day. He wandered to the side of the building, searching for a ladder.

There was no ladder, but there was an empty trash can. He stared at it for a moment, then carefully, quietly took off the lid, turned it upside down, and carried it back to the oak. Once he was standing on it, it was only one long heave into the belly of the tree.

Branches snagged his jacket, and for a moment he lay winded, irritated beyond measure that he could be this badly out of shape. Still breathing heavily, he looked up. The yard light glowed brightly enough for him to see her window through the thick-fingered branches. They would hold his weight; that wasn't a problem. Not having climbed a tree in many long years was the real problem, and his attitude toward heights had always been less than enthusiastic.

He shimmied forward along the strongest branch. A limb caught at his jeans; another tried to tangle in his hair. He lost his hat. In time, though, in methodical good time, he gained enough yardage so that he could reach out and touch her window. After that, he took several seconds to catch his breath and wipe the dampness from his brow.

He finally worked up the courage to rap once, then twice on the pane, very softly. So softly that he couldn't believe it when the window was promptly thrown open.

By eleven that night, Carroll had been buried beneath three comforters in bed with a heating pad on her stomach. She was freezing. Nightmares were dancing on her walls.

It had been years since she'd missed a day of work. The only reason she hadn't gone in that morning was that she hadn't been able to sit up without cringing.

Now she didn't really feel that bad. Actually, she felt increasingly wonderful, lightheaded and free and dreamy. Moonlight filtered in the window, making increasingly strange shapes on her bedroom wall.

Moonlight and dreams gradually blended together. She was making love with Alan under the cool trickle of a waterfall. Both of them were naked, their flesh slick and cool . . . instants later, the waterfall and Alan were gone and something dark and terrifying was chasing her in the night, chasing her with a torch, so hot, so hot . . . and then the weirdest dream of all, of a tall, dark stranger rapping on her window. Silly, her bedroom window was on the second floor, but the rapping continued, and in the dream it seemed perfectly natural to float out of bed, fly to the window, and throw it open to the crisp, cold night and her ravisher.

"Hi there," Carroll said seductively. "I've been waiting for you."

Wonderful air as cold as ice rushed over her over-heated skin from the opened window. She shivered from her toes to her soul in response. She'd had ravishment dreams before, but never as good as this one. The tall, dark stranger was turning into Alan, the best part of all. Some kidnapping dreams could pall when her seducer wasn't real. Alan was deliciously real. He was also taking far too long to climb in her window.

"Waiting for me?" Dark eyes peered in, dazzling her with their intensity.

"All my life," she said blithely. "Hurry. I love you." Anticipation danced in her bloodstream. Exhilaration, laughter, and champagne danced along with it. In the dream, she'd had liters and liters of champagne and no inhibitions at all. Heat was pouring from her nerve endings, pure female, lusty heat. She slipped her fingers through her hair, shaking the tousled mop in seductive invitation.

There was another slight hesitation, then one jeaned leg slid through the opening, then a long, bent-over body. "I love"—then the last leg—"you, too." The window slammed behind him. Breathing heavily for a moment, Alan rubbed his hands on the backs of his jeans to rid them of bark and leaf debris, then stood there in silence. His voice finally pierced the darkness, low and hoarse. "Caro, I *do* love you. I've loved you for so long. I know this must look crazy . . ."

"No!" Her ravisher was shy, delighting her. "It's not at all crazy." She rushed forward on the thinnest carpet of air, slipping her arms around his waist. His jacket was freezing against her long flannel night-

gown, for an instant shocking her, disturbing the sensations she was enjoying in the dream. Her fever-clogged brain refused the intrusion of reality. "Nothing's crazy between the two of us. Take me, Alan!"

She rose up on tiptoe, sealing his cold lips with her own. With brazen freedom, she rocked her pelvis against him, let her wanton fingers rush through his hair and tighten. It took no time at all to warm his lips, no time at all for her kidnapper to pick up the spirit of devil-may-care seduction.

In the darkness, she could hear his change in breathing, reveled in it. Huge hands caressed from her back to her bottom and stopped there, holding her dancing hips still, molding them high and hard against him. His tongue dipped into her mouth, providing her with moisture she hadn't known she was desperate for.

"Caro . . . ah, Caro. You just can't know . . ."

Such wonderful hands he had, dozens of them. Roaming her back, sliding over her slim shoulders, brushing with teasing pressure on her breasts, up to that softest hollow in her throat. "Caro," he breathed again, and she felt deliriously high. She'd wanted this for so long. Those fingers of his touched her face as he kissed her and kept on kissing her, a whispery touch that explored her cheeks, her closed eyelids, her forehead.

"Caro?" A flat hand suddenly pressed itself against her forehead. *"Carroll!"*

He tore himself away from her so fast she was left bereft, her arms still reaching for him. Her bedside lamp was switched on, and her dream took an abrupt, nightmarish turn. No decent dream would leave her stranded, wearing a long, bulky nightgown with white athletic socks. She immediately lunged for the light and switched it off. The darkness was better, but not quite as good as before. Something was going wrong very fast.

Actually, everything was going very wrong very fast. She was no longer blazingly hot but chilled. A fit of trembling took her body by storm, and she felt damp and dizzy, but no longer nice-dizzy. A knife seemed to be lodged in her brain, slicing away, and her ravisher was no longer murmuring sweet nothings but a steady refrain of "dammit, dammit, dammit" as he moved around the room.

He changed the litany momentarily to "Caro, just *stay* there," when he pushed her into a chair.

She heard the sound of his jacket flung against the wall, the incredibly loud switch-on of the overhead light. She winced at the cruel blaze of light. Confusion made everything surrealistic, like part of a dream. It *had* to be a dream. Logically, she simply had to reach for that champagne high again, that delicious heat . . . and there wasn't anything logical about Alan stripping the sheets from her bed and swearing colorfully as he unplugged the heating pad.

One instant he was on the far side of the room, and the next instant he was kneeling in front of her, his dark blue eyes relentless, piercing, as fathomless as those of the pirate lover in some historical novel. He was furious, the rational part of her brain told her, but that dreaming part of Carroll heard his voice, gentle, tender, as soothing as velvet. "I'm going to take your nightgown off, love. You'll be far more comfortable in a dry one."

Maybe true, but the nightgown he'd pulled from her drawer was old, faded, and insufferably prim. "I'd prefer," she whispered, "the pink one with lace."

"Pardon?"

"The pink one. Alan, I'm *not* making love to you in *that* nightgown."

"Ah. Sweetheart, when we make love you won't be wearing anything, so it hardly makes any difference. And in the meantime, raise your arms."

She wasn't inclined to comply. Another *dammit* escaped under his breath before Alan could stop it. He lifted her arms and tugged off the long, damp nightgown. Beneath it, she was bare and shivering.

Horror rushed through her. "Turn around!"

"Caro, this is *me*. *Me*. Relax," he said impatiently.

"It isn't that. It's the socks. No way am I going to be naked except for socks." She bent down too quickly; the knife sliced clear through her skull. Stupid. How stupid. There was suddenly no dream to cling to, just this horrid thick dizziness, a body that felt battered, and somewhere, yes, an obstinate trace of vanity. She really did want the darned socks off.

His chuckle startled her, and so did the swift brush of lips on her forehead, followed all too rapidly by her arms being slipped into the fresh nightgown.

"I can—" she started to say, but he was paying no attention.

"Hush. Let me. And someday," he said gently, "I'm going to make love to you with just your socks on, to show you how silly you are. You're sexy to me no matter what you're wearing, kitten, and you always will be. Now try to think clearly."

She was thinking clearly. That was the problem.

"Where's your thermometer?"

She couldn't think *that* clearly.

"All right. I'll find it. Now, have you taken aspirin?"

He urged her into bed, a feat that didn't take much coaxing. He seemed to have stolen all her blankets except the comforter, which wasn't enough to keep her warm. She tried to tell him, but he popped a thermometer into her mouth.

Five thousand years from now, when she regained her sense of humor, she was going to tell Alan that he was rapidly losing credibility as a ravisher. He grabbed her hand, but it wasn't a loverlike hold. His two fingers were pressed to her wrist, and with the other hand he was smoothing back her hair. She pushed her hair forward again, the way it was supposed to go. Otherwise, it would stand straight up. Nothing more ghastly than hair standing up every which way; she looked bad enough.

"Would you stop fighting me," he scolded, and released her wrist. "And if I ever discover you've gone to bed with a plugged-in heating pad again, you'll be in big trouble."

She didn't know when he'd dropped the gentle voice, but when he read the temperature on the thermometer he looked vaguely as if he might shoot her.

"A hundred and three degrees. A hundred and three degrees, and you didn't call me!"

"I feel fine," she assured him.

"You feel like *hell*."

"A little," she admitted. "Alan, don't go . . ."

"I'm not going anywhere. You may be. Now answer quick, and no more nonsense. Throat sore?"

She shook her head.

"Your stomach?"

She shook her head.

"Caro," he said patiently, "you had a heating pad on. Did you have stomach cramps? Have you kept food down? Diarrhea?"

He'd folded back her blanket and was poking her lower abdomen, paying no attention to the mortified flush that climbed her cheeks. The pallor beneath the flush seemed the only thing that fascinated him.

"No, no, and no! Stop that. Darn it, Alan, every kid in school has the same stupid flu. A high fever and aches and pains and that's it. I am *fine,* and my glands are *wonderful,* thank you." She pushed his hands away from the swollen nodules in her throat.

"My four-year-olds make better patients than you do," Alan informed her, and stood up, readjusting the covers around her chin. "I'm going to get you something to drink and some aspirin . . . what's that?" He motioned to the glass by her bed.

"Whiskey with honey and lemon. My mother's cure for everything that ails you."

"You didn't drink any."

"I hate whiskey."

"Never drink it when you have the flu," he muttered. "Just puts sugar in the blood, kitten. Worst thing you could do. Now, stay there."

He wagged his finger at her, as if he thought she might rush off. She couldn't imagine why she was happy he was there. He was treating her like one of his four-year-old patients; she did *not* want the glass of orange juice he bullied her into drinking, and embarrassing fragments of an extremely silly dream were gradually filtering back to her. She tried to apologize, but all Alan could talk about was how relieved he was that her fever was breaking. She'd been a lot happier when the fever was raging. Now she felt truly awful.

Still, when he turned out the light, she panicked. "You're not going home?"

"No." In the darkness, he shucked off his clothes and slid into bed beside her. Gently, he turned her on her side, facing away from him, and tucked her spoon fashion against his chest and bent knees before pulling the light cover up to her chin. With a sigh, he settled down. His arms slid firmly around her waist. "I guarantee," he murmured, "to keep you warm, Caro."

Fuzzy, woolly darkness enclosed her. She suddenly didn't feel nearly as bad, just sleepy and a little achy and impossibly cuddly. Her eyes closed, and she nestled her back more firmly against Alan's bare chest. His beard nuzzled her neck for a moment as he bestowed a surprise of a kiss, and then there was silence.

Just before she fell asleep, she murmured, "Alan, did I dream all of it?"

"Hmmm?"

"I dreamed you climbed in the window."

"Caro," Alan said gently, "you were delirious."

"But I know I locked the door. I always lock the—"

"Sssh. Sleep now. You need rest."

Chapter 7

CARROLL STRETCHED, YAWNED, and sleepily opened her eyes . . . then blinked. A shaggy bear seemed to be lying next to her. A huge, warm shaggy bear with disheveled brown hair and a brown beard and alert blue eyes. "G'morning," she said groggily.

"Feel better?"

She nodded and snuggled closer. Climbing mountains in Shades Park now seemed like a terrible idea, but the lead was gone from her head, and her body was no longer creaking and groaning. She simply felt on a basic empathic level with a mop. Her cheek burrowed against Alan's bare warm chest. She saw no particular reason to move from that spot all day.

"You're not wearing a stitch of clothes," she mentioned.

"No."

"*Nothing.*"

Alan reached under the covers, captured her wandering hand, and pinned it against his chest. He never blinked an eye.

She smiled sleepily, and her eyelids drifted closed again. Vague memories of the night before began wandering through her consciousness, most of them running a fine line between mortification and embarrassment. Since she couldn't pretend they hadn't happened, owning up seemed like the only sensible choice. "I'm sorry, Alan," she said quietly.

"Hey. Don't be silly." His thumb stroked her cheek. "Are you *ever* going to get ill like that again without calling me?"

"No, sir."

"The fever's gone, kitten."

"And I feel wonderful." To prove it, she slid her arms around his bare waist and sneaked a flannel-covered leg between his. She'd wasted hours, having him naked in bed with her and not even knowing it. And after all those months of postponing intimacy, she could no longer remember a single reason why. It felt perfectly natural waking up with Alan.

It felt even more natural to touch him. He was built along the lines of Gibraltar, strong and solid. The parts of Alan she'd touched before didn't begin to make up the whole. He had sprinkles of wiry hair on his chest, not a lot of it. A flat abdomen, no rear end to speak of, strongly muscular legs. All of those parts appealed to her, but the whole was the surprise. Alan added up to a physically beautiful man. She'd never really thought about it before.

Nor had she ever realized he was so responsive to her touch. His pulse leaped when her palm touched his nipple. His skin warmed when her hands strayed down to his ribs and abdomen. And she found her hands gently pinned when they tried to stray lower. Blue eyes bore into her, focused on her mischievous smile.

"When," he murmured, "did the lady get so brazen?"

"I think she was brazen all along. Maybe she has

always had a latent sensual streak, just waiting for a chance to break out."

"I like it."

"I'm glad."

"If you weren't still sick," he said firmly.

"I'm not ill anymore," she assured him.

"So you think. But you haven't tried to get out of bed yet."

"The last thing I want to do is get out of bed."

"Caro . . ." Alan suddenly wasn't smiling. He released her hands and leaned over her, pushing back her hair, studying her forehead and eyes and eyebrows and temples and cheeks, savoring, loving. "Once you're well, once I seriously get you in bed," he said quietly, "I may never let you out of it. Know that."

A lump formed in her throat. She reached up to touch his bearded cheek. "I love you, Alan."

"And I love you. More than I can ever seem to find the words to tell you."

She shook her head. "I never needed words. But I needed"—she hesitated—"to be sure."

"Of me?"

"Maybe of myself, of us." She made her tone deceptively light. "I always wanted to be one of those assertive women who blithely jump into bed whenever they feel like it, who don't hesitate to express their own sexual needs and feelings. There's only a thin line between those women and me. I'd like to tell you that line has something to do with high standards, but in truth it has more to do with cowardice."

"Cowardice?" Alan echoed.

She snuggled closer. "First times, darn it. First

times aren't fun. First times are made up of worrying that things won't go well and worrying about what your partner thinks of your body, and worrying about doing the right things, saying the right things . . ."

For a moment, Alan was quiet; then he probed gently. "He hurt you, didn't he, Caro?"

"Who?"

"A man. Sometime. Your first?"

She closed her eyes, feeling oddly shy. "It was years ago, and shouldn't matter anymore, but ever since then . . . Love's supposed to take away the inhibitions, but for me it makes them worse. It isn't sex that scares me, Alan; it's just that I worry about the first time. I just . . . didn't want you to walk away."

"Caro, look at me." He gently nudged her chin up with his hand. "First times for a man are made of worrying he won't perform to the lady's needs and satisfaction. Worrying she'll discover his paunch. Worrying he won't find those particular things that turn her on, those things that happen so naturally between lovers who know each other."

She waited a moment, absorbed what he had told her, realized that it was the same for him as it was for her. "You don't," she ventured finally, "have a paunch. And I wouldn't care if you had."

"And you have a beautiful body, woman."

"You haven't seen it yet," she reminded him.

"I saw it last night."

"You weren't even looking then. You were busy bullying me into wearing this horrible nightgown—"

"You have to be joking," he said dryly. "You have a tiny mole just under your right breast." His lips brushed her cheek. "A faint scar on your lower abdomen, less than an inch, the size of a sliver." He kissed her throat, then traced a line of kisses up into her hair. "The tips of your breasts are a dusky rose, not brown. Tiny nipples. And on the inside of your left thigh . . ."

"Alan." Color was rising in her cheeks faster than a river in a flood.

"It's going to be fine between us, Caro." He leaned back again and possessively tucked the covers around her. "If I'd known that was all you were worried about, we would have been in bed long before this."

It wasn't all. Carroll touched his cheek, remembering fears that the sexual spark wasn't strong enough between them, wanting some kind of guarantee that what they had was enough to last for a lifetime, and yes, wanting something more than a love that had happened so easily.

The spark was there, hot enough to burn her. The compatibility and honesty were there; she could never have shared feelings like this with another man. And for weeks now she'd suffered that agony-ecstasy of being in love—a feeling she'd been afraid she'd never experience. "What about you?" she asked quietly. "Alan, you must have had doubts about me, about what we are together."

"A few in the beginning—but you won me over awfully fast," he teased lightly, but his smile didn't quite reach his eyes. A fear of first times might have been part of the reason she'd shied away from intimacy with him. He knew that wasn't all. All along, he'd suspected that her strongest hesitations had to do with doubts about him and about her feelings for him. Now would be the best of times to coax her to talk about these feelings . . . except that the lady tucked so neatly beneath him still had ashen skin and eyes with a lingering fever brightness. "I hate to say this," he drawled.

"What?"

He kissed her nose. "I have a date with little Susie's adenoids in two hours. And you're going to eat breakfast before I leave, which means . . ."

"You want me to let you up." Her arms tightened firmly around him.

"And *after* I bring you breakfast in bed"—he gave her a playful tap on her behind—"we're going to see how sassy you are when you try to walk. Two bits says you can't make it to the bathroom and back without wobbling. And once I go, you have strict orders to stay in bed all day, doing nothing but sleeping and drinking fluids and taking aspirin. Caro, if I find you dressed when I come back at dinnertime, you're going to be in big trouble."

"You've been threatening me with big trouble ever since you came in last night," she remarked with total unconcern. One eyebrow lifted suddenly. "Alan, you *did* come in that window."

Alan slid out of bed and reached for his clothes. "We're back to that again? Grown men do not come in windows."

"I *know* the door was locked. And maybe I was a little muzzy-headed . . ."

"You were more than muzzy-headed. You thought you could fly."

Carroll propped the pillows up behind her, never

taking her eyes from his face. "You know," she said slowly, "that was probably the most romantic dream I've ever had . . . a dark stranger suddenly appearing at my window on a black night." She motioned him silent with her hand. "Yes, yes, I know. I just *imagined* it was you. And I guess I *was* pretty out of it, because I remember the strangest sensations. This incredible delight that a tall dark stranger would go to so much trouble. And this thrilling, breathless anticipation of being ravished, of not feeling the least bit threatened. Actually, maybe that's not so strange. I mean, only a tall, dark stranger who loved me very much—who was capable of an incredible amount of love—could think up such a . . ." She smiled at his expression. "Never mind, never mind. I know it wasn't you."

Alan tugged his dark sweater on, shaking his head as he walked to the door. "I swear, Caro, you have a vivid imagination. You'll do anything to keep me out of the kitchen, won't you? I can handle scrambled eggs, I swear it."

"Yes."

"Furthermore, you should have storms put on those windows."

"Yes."

"A burglar could easily reach you by climbing that tree."

"Yes."

"And as for a nice, demure woman having dreams like that . . ." He shook his head in despair. "You've shocked me. Seriously shocked me."

"Sorry," she said gravely. "Better wipe that grin off your face, Alan."

"I'll do that."

But she heard his burst of laughter all the way from the kitchen.

She survived Tuesday, joined the living on Wednesday, and felt unquestionably human by Thursday . . . having little choice in the matter. Her momentum to get well arose from a man solicitously feeding her gourmet Vietnamese, Hungarian, and Peruvian specialties. Not only was her kitchen never going to recover, but Carroll came back to life out of sheer hunger.

Just home from school on Friday, still wearing her coat, she grabbed a carrot stick from the refrigerator and munched on it as she dialed the number of Alan's office. She'd already tried to reach him twice from work. Both times he'd been with patients.

The man deserved to be paid back for the care he'd given her for the past three nights. Her refrigerator was still stocked with more citrus juices than she could drink in a lifetime. He'd brought her daffodils. He'd bullied her into staying in bed as if she were some kind of invalid; then he'd beaten her at Scrabble. And if he hadn't stayed with her those nights, at least he'd stayed until she fell asleep . . . and if she didn't fall asleep at an hour early enough to suit him, he'd read her medical journals, the content of which was enough to cure the most hardened insomniac.

There wasn't the slimmest chance she would let him know if she ever caught a sniffle again. Safer yet, she'd just stay permanently healthy. In the meantime, she had in mind repaying him by blowing her month's budget on the most expensive dinner in town . . . as soon as she caught up with the man.

"I'm afraid he took off for the hospital," June Goodman told her wearily. "That man is harder to track down than a roadrunner in the desert."

"Are you expecting him back this afternoon?" Carroll asked.

"No, he canceled his last afternoon appointment before he went to the hospital—this was an emergency." June paused. "Carroll?"

"Yes?" Her lips were already tugging into a smile. Alan's nurse was irrepressible.

"I figured by now you'd have exerted some influence and gotten him to shave off that beard."

Carroll chuckled, still munching on her carrot. "I keep thinking he'll get tired of it."

"Well, unfortunately, he's decided that you like it. I told him if he was going to skate on ice that thin, he'd better be prepared to walk on water. Listen, you need any help from me, you just say so. I've been managing that man for six years now. The trick is nagging him, pure and simple. He can't stand it."

Carroll laughed again. "I never did perfect the fine art of nagging."

"I know. That's why he loves you. All right, now . . . I'll leave him a message you called just in case he does come back here."

Hanging up, Carroll decided to catch Alan at dinner time. For an hour or two, it didn't matter anyway. The apartment was begging for a vacuuming, and clothes were piled up in the hamper. She'd let things go while she had the flu.

Two hours later, the apartment was clean, and Carroll was blissfully luxuriating in a hot shower when the phone rang. Grabbing a towel, she hustled for the phone.

The caller was a man with a baritone so gloomy and distracted that she didn't initially recognize it as Alan's. "Sorry, I missed you earlier, kitten."

Abruptly, she stopped rubbing her wet hair with a towel. "Rough day?"

"Fine."

He didn't sound as if he'd had a fine day; he sounded as if he'd been in the front lines of a war. All the more reason, Carroll concluded, to take him out for a quiet dinner. But when she voiced the invitation, there was an unexpected hesitation at the other end.

"Caro, there's nothing I'd like more . . . but I'm honestly beat. Will tomorrow be all right?"

"Of course," she said warmly.

But it wasn't. The minute she hung up the phone, she knew it wasn't. Alan was entitled to time to himself, and he was also entitled to be tired, but the tone of his voice hadn't been just weary or preoccupied. He'd sounded seriously depressed, and Alan wasn't a moody man.

In her bedroom, she pulled on old jeans and a sweat shirt, then reached for a hair dryer. He's entitled to a low day, too, just like the rest of the human race, she mentally informed herself, but fifteen minutes later she was picking up her car keys. *If he'd wanted to talk something out, he would have said so. Haven't you ever simply wanted to be alone? Of course you have.*

She picked up her purse. *Carroll, he's seen you for three days running and given you every free min-*

ute he's had. Give the man a break.

Actually, she had every intention of giving him a break. She'd back out lickety-split if he showed the first sign of simply wanting solitude, but she had to see him. She had a very distressing picture in her head of Alan sitting alone in a dark apartment through the long hours of the night, needing someone and with no one there. The picture wouldn't go away.

Besides, there was the question of health. His health. Alone with only his own cooking talents, there was no telling what he'd feed himself. On the way, she picked up some food from a takeout Chinese restaurant.

Balancing two bags filled with white cartons, Carroll rapped on the door of Alan's ground-floor apartment and waited. When there was no answer, she turned around and again identified Alan's red Fiero in the lot. He was definitely home. Frowning, she cocked her head to look through his living room bay window, but the view from the steps revealed only that all the lights were off and that his favorite recliner was unoccupied.

After knocking one more time, she tried the doorknob and pushed. The door wasn't locked. Inside, she found only dusky darkness and total silence. "Alan?" she called softly, and stepped in.

Adjusting the packages in her arms, she switched on a lamp to dispel the late evening gloom, then continued to the kitchen. From the doorway, she saw him, his elbows on the kitchen table and his face in his hands.

Her heart ached as if she were the despairing one.

Loving him made his hurt hers. She didn't need to know the nature of the problem. Actually, she didn't need to know anything at all. "Hey, you," she said softly.

His head jerked up instantly. His shoulders squared, exhaustion was banished from his features, and an almost-smile touched his mouth as he stood up. She could have kicked him. More than that, she could have kicked herself, for so belatedly realizing how often and successfully he hid his real feelings.

"I didn't hear you come in," Alan said.

"Of course you didn't hear me. I was tiptoeing—and don't worry that I'm going to stay. You said you were tired—so am I," she lied. "Which was when it occurred to me that you might not feel like fixing a meal. So . . ." She motioned to the bags full of Chinese food. "I'll get the plates and silverware. Beer?"

He shook his head. "I'm out. I think there's some milk."

"That'll do. Want to eat in front of the TV?"

He hesitated. He honestly wanted no one anywhere around him, least of all Carroll. He wasn't in a romantic mood. He felt as exciting as yesterday's newspaper, and he doubted he could follow a conversation, much less be the kind of man any woman would want for company.

In that short time he'd hesitated, though, Carroll had whisked past him. She turned on the lamps in the living room and tuned into the news on TV. Then she pushed aside the coffee table and dragged the huge pillows in front of the couch to serve as footrests.

Five minutes later, she was stealing war sui gui from his plate. It was the first chance he'd taken to really look at her. Her legs were curled under her, and she wasn't wearing a trace of makeup. Her hair was freshly washed, and soft little spikes wisped around her face. "I'm leaving right after the news," she promised him.

When the news was over, she mentioned that she was leaving right after the rerun of *M*A*S*H*. But when that was over, she was busy rinsing the dishes in his kitchen. She returned to the living room carrying his mail and the paper. Handing him the front page and sports section along with the mail, she took the women's section and crossword and flopped down in his recliner.

"I'm leaving right after this," she told him.

By then, he knew well enough that she wasn't leaving. She didn't say a word, his brown-eyed witch, just lay in that chair with her legs dangling over the side and scratched on the puzzle.

At ten she made popcorn—unhealthfully, lavishly slathered with butter, exactly the way he liked it— and propped herself against a pillow at his feet, frequently lifting the popcorn bowl so he could reach it. *Rocky* was on the tube, a rerun. Sylvester hadn't changed from the first airing. He remained unwashed, misunderstood, and macho.

"Caro . . ." Alan said finally.

She shushed him, bringing the first smile to his face in hours. Not that she didn't have a right to enjoy the movie, but she was staring in fascination at the commercial for a deodorant. Such a maneuvering woman. And as if he'd invited her there, she suddenly stood up, stretched, and made it look perfectly logical for her then to resettle next to him on the couch. Her fanny close to his pelvis, her cheek pressed to his shoulder. Her eyes never once left the screen.

He found himself playing with her hair, a strand at a time. It smelled like spring and felt like silk. Her skin was warm when he tucked her to his side, her head on his chest, her thighs close to his. Her breathing was as even and regular as a ticking clock.

He closed his eyes, suddenly needing her next to him the way he needed air, water, food. Her being there didn't change anything. He still felt grief well up in him like a flood, like a cold, dark wall too high to climb. He needed to deal with those feelings alone, the way he'd always dealt with them, but if Carroll had tried to leave, he knew he would have stopped her.

She didn't try to leave. In time, she simply reached for his remote control switch and turned off the sound. The climax of the picture was a streak of color and action, undoubtedly a tribute to misunderstood macho men everywhere. He barely noticed, wasn't even aware she'd turned off the sound.

"I delivered a little boy around five years ago," he said quietly, just as if they'd been having a conversation.

Carroll didn't turn around to face him. "You're not usually involved in obstetrics, are you?"

"No, this was an emergency. I can still remember the day this scrawny little man bolted into my office as if demons were after him, claiming his wife was in labor and there wasn't time to get her to the hospital. They lived right across the street, and the hospital isn't that far from here—I tried to tell him, to calm him down, but he wasn't listening. He *couldn't* listen; he was coming apart at the seams. And he was right, she'd been in labor for hours but had thought it was another false alarm — the contractions were irregular, Caro; there wasn't time."

"A healthy baby?"

"Very. I'll never forget what a hurry that boy was in to rush into life . . . Jonathan Roberts was his name. He was my patient from that day. I watched him grow. He was such a pistol, never gave his parents a moment's rest. Nothing halfway about him; with Jonathan it was always all or nothing. Colic and the terrible two's, nasty little temper and big brown eyes. Ever know a kid to get kicked out of nursery school?"

Carroll turned then, quietly, her eyes on Alan's face. "No," she said lightly. His features were calm. He showed no sign of pain or emotion. He showed nothing at all. From the tone of his voice, he could have been matter of factly discussing the weather.

"Jonathan managed it. He was bright, but such a devil. He would have started kindergarten this year. Except that in July, his mother brought him to me for a checkup."

She said nothing, afraid to move, afraid to breathe. Alan wasn't looking at her. His fingers were threading in her hair, over and over, his touch impossibly gentle. Nothing had changed in his expression. Only because she was intensely aware of him could she pick up that slight shakiness in his fingers. And his tone . . . When he started talking again, the words took an effort.

"I sent him to a neurologist, a friend of mine. I

wish I hadn't been absolutely sure what was wrong, but I *was* absolutely sure. At one time, I considered specializing in pediatric neurology, even did my internship in that field. Barker's the best man there is, but I knew when the boy went in that his chances were never better than fifty-fifty."

"Alan . . ." she whispered.

"A good doctor," Alan spat out, flat and hard, "remains objective about these things. A doctor who loses his objectivity has no business practicing medicine. That's a simple fact. In time, we'll know more. And in the meantime, we help those we can. That's the way it has to be. No exceptions." He added absently, "I was waiting for Barker when he got out of surgery with the boy this afternoon."

She didn't ask what had happened. She knew. Tears welled up in her eyes as she reached for Alan. As if her slightest touch triggered a fuse, the muscles in his face tightened, the color drained from his face, and his eyes were a blaze of anger and frustration and bitterness and grief.

"Dammit," he said fiercely. "Damn everything. Dammitall to hell. There was nothing I could do."

Chapter 8

THOUGH HER TOUCH had been gentle, Alan instantly withdrew from her. Physically, he moved only inches away, jerking himself up to a sitting position with his face averted. Emotionally, though, Carroll could feel the distance he was determined to create between them. The glare of lamplight showed his rigid profile and the lines of strain and frustration on his face. His eyes were remote, as blue as ice, a thousand miles away from her.

For a few seconds, she felt helpless. There was so much she wanted to say . . . that there was nothing Alan could have done, that he hadn't even been involved in the operation, that he was the best of doctors because he *did* care. She said nothing. Words could never be adequate, not for this.

And she couldn't bear those eyes. Instinct made her reach for him again. Though he stiffened, though she felt that sharp sting of rejection very clearly, she still ventured closer . . . close enough to touch her lips to his.

"Look," he rasped. "Forget I told you any of it, would you? Just—"

She heard the leave-me-alone tone in his voice. So he didn't want comfort? He was so very sure he didn't want comfort. Pressing her hand to the back of

his head, she touched his lips with hers again, and so
fast, like the touch of flame to tinder, found fire.

Oh, Alan, she thought fleetingly. *You didn't really
think I'd let you be alone right now?*

His mouth groped blindly on hers, and she found
herself crushed, enclosed very suddenly in steel man-
acles. His right hand clenched in her hair, and his
other arm wrapped itself tightly around her—too
tightly—as if she were a treasure trying to escape
him, as if she would spring free if he gave her a
moment to breathe.

She wasn't going anywhere.

Her mouth was acquiescent beneath his, accepting
the fierce pressure of his lips and inviting more. It
wasn't a kiss of passion but the kiss of a man lost and
trying to find something to hold on to. She tasted
frustration and grief. She tasted a man who could
accept neither very well, a man who would never
accept loss easily. All she could do was be there.
Willingly, her mouth cushioned his. Willingly, she
absorbed the bruising seal he made of their lips until
she could barely breathe. He didn't seem to notice,
and she certainly didn't care.

His hands were suddenly everywhere, desperately
seeking skin. Needing warmth. She felt her sweat
shirt being pushed up, then the tug of her bra until the
catch sprang open.

Her spine sank into the cushions as they both fell
back. Where he was rigid, she offered her own softness. For the anger and pain exploding inside him,
she returned supple pliancy. And when his palm too
roughly kneaded a breast, she arched to make that
breast easy for him to touch. His leg sliced between

hers. She simply clamped her legs around him, wooing him closer.

Blood pounded in her veins, but no fear. If Alan had no control, she had all the power of a woman, of instincts, of loving. Lamplight flooded his face, then shadow. Her eyes absorbed every changing expression on his face. She saw sorrow and blind loss, and felt the intense aloneness of a man who just didn't know what to do with the pain. His eyes were squeezed closed and his breath hoarse and uneven. So generous in giving to others, Alan was so damned harsh to Alan.

Slipping an arm under his, she managed to find the first button of his shirt, then the second. Then the third. The instant her palm slid over his bare chest, his body went rigid. His eyes shot open, and he pushed her hands away. "God. *No,* Caro."

"Yes."

"*No.* I never meant . . . Caro, I would never hurt you. Dammit, I don't know what I was thinking of. Never like this . . ."

"Yes. Just like this," she whispered patiently, and unfastened the remaining buttons before pushing his shirt open.

Again, he dragged her hands away. "Never rough. Not with you. That's never what I want for you, and the first time . . ."

"*Yes,*" she said fiercely. "I told you all about my fear of first times. Only you can forget it. We can go through all that tomorrow night, or next year, or when we're a hundred and three."

"Carroll—"

"*Hush.*" She could have cried with frustration.

The fastening on his slacks wouldn't give.

And he wasn't helping. He didn't do anything to interfere with her unhooking the catch at his waist, but he was totally still for a moment or two. Not long, and then he suddenly dropped a kiss on her mouth. A soft kiss that made up for all the rough ones. A beguiling kiss that sent a trickle of champagne fizzling up and down her veins.

Her fingers stopped their fumbling. Instants earlier, she'd been in a terrible hurry to get his clothes off, to get her clothes off, to have the man inside her where she could hold him as close as a woman could hold a man. Sex had nothing to do with it. She would just as willingly have climbed mountains or turned cartwheels if she'd thought it would erase the grief and frustration and anger in his eyes. Loving Alan was the only thing that mattered, and the last thing she'd paid attention to had been her own sexual feelings.

She paid attention to them now. Silky flames lapped at her nerve endings until her skin felt like toast, hot on the outside, buttery-soft within. Every place he'd touched roughly he was now comforting. His palm stroked up and down her spine, a no-hurry whisper caress that made her shiver. His lips sought the pulse points in her wrist, her temples, her throat, courting her slow, lazy, sleepy heartbeat. Maybe her heart wasn't even beating?

It had to be. She was very definitely alive. Her vision was momentarily blocked when he slipped her sweat shirt over her head. He was looking into her eyes when he dropped it, such an intense look that her skin burned and she couldn't seem to look away.

Alan pushed the loose bra straps from her shoulders, then ducked down, nudging them the rest of the way with his cheek, his mouth, the soft licks of his tongue.

Bare, her breasts that had been so roughly caressed were now wooed with the warmth of his hands. He teased the tip of her right breast between two fingers, then methodically, meticulously ensured that the left received equal attention. His beard . . . she really couldn't bear his beard. It scraped and tickled and bristled, and he rubbed it deliberately in the hollow between her breasts.

She was suddenly in a hurry again, only this time for completely different reasons. "Alan . . ."

He shifted up, silencing her. Her lips were sensitive from his earlier kisses, maybe oversensitive to any touch now, but she'd never felt a kiss like that from Alan. Zero gravity. Earthquakes. Impossible things. She told herself that her inhibitions would undoubtedly return any minute. For now, she soared for his kiss. Wantonly, she pushed aside his shirt so she could rub her breasts against his chest, reached down with mindless abandon for the fastening on his pants again . . . and still couldn't manage it.

"Alan. You have to help."

"You're doing"—his kiss whispered over her collarbone—"just fine."

"It's some kind of hook. I'm afraid it'll rip—"

"Let it."

The hook came free in her hand. Alan rewarded her with yet another kiss, and they were suddenly both shedding pants, shoes, whatever it was that still separated them.

The thing was, she wasn't Carroll. Carroll was welcome to go teach speech on Monday morning; she was someone else entirely. His wonderful couch was far too soft. The carpet was better. She felt the graze of crinkly wool against her back, then her side, then on no part of her body at all because she was on top of him. And he suddenly convulsed with laughter, bewildering her.

"Caro," he rasped, *"not* on the nipples, you . . ."

She promptly licked his nipples again, suffered wonderful retribution when he applied his tongue to her navel, turned her over with consummate ease, and kissed the dimple on her fanny. She paid him back in kind by kissing the back of his knee. Any minute now, she'd get serious about this. Sex was a very, very serious business. She'd always known that.

And it suddenly was very serious, because smiles met smiles from inches away, touched down in a kiss like no other kiss, made the smiles disappear but not the specialness. Simple light became brilliant light. Laughter hushed. And an ache rocked through her, fierce and compelling, not funny at all.

He eased inside her. She'd been empty forever, was suddenly full, so much so that she thought he was hurting her . . . but it was just the ache, growing until she thought it would split her in two. The gentleman above her might have been delicate enough to close his eyes . . . but he didn't.

And she watched him as he watched her. Their limbs interwove, her legs wrapped around his, and her hands relished the slick, smooth warmth of his skin as he started the rhythm. She knew the song.

Although she'd never heard it before, she knew the song. It soared in her veins, on her skin, through the night. She ached from the wanting, from the need that brazenly claimed her flesh, her heart. A civil war could have taken place outside the window, and still she watched his eyes.

His eyes were love-blue, a color she'd never come across before.

She loved his eyes.

Ecstasy rippled through her with the brilliance and light of a firecracker, never expected, not like this. She felt his flow of life, heard his harsh, helpless cry, tasted love in the kiss he gave her. Such a gift. Such a celebration.

"Kitten, I'm too heavy for you."

"No, you're not."

"I'll crush your ribs."

"You have my permission." But she reluctantly opened one sleepy eye. She didn't know what time it was, but it was late enough for Bela Lugosi to be on the tube. Actually, the carpet was a little scratchy, and the only parts of her that were warm were the ones Alan was covering. "We just made love on the floor," she remarked.

"You noticed that?"

"Your bed can't be thirty feet away from here." Her gaze focused on Alan's face. A shock of hair had fallen over his forehead; he looked sleepier than she felt; and she really had to do something about that grin. "I'm pretty sure it's your fault we never made it to the bed," she said severely.

"Yours. You attacked me, remember?"

"You must have misinterpreted my actions. I've never attacked a man in my entire life."

His tone softened. "Haven't you, Caro?" He shifted off her, stood up, yawned, and reached for her hand. Once he had her hand, he wouldn't let it go. She had to trail after him, holding hands, from the living room to the kitchen to the hall, while he turned off the TV, lamps, and lights, then locked up for the night.

His bedroom was dark. She'd seen it in daylight and knew the oak wardrobe and bureau were on opposite walls, that a writing desk was under the window, that his double bed was an oak-spiraled four-poster. She didn't need to see. Alan guided her through the darkness, never releasing her hand. "Can't let you go," he said simply.

The texture of the spread they pulled down felt strange to her, somehow not what she remembered. And the sheets shocked her bare skin; the fabric was satiny and cold. Such things passed out of her mind as fast as they entered it. Alan wrapped her up as soon as they were in bed, not in sheets or covers, but in himself, in legs and arms and chest, in the smell and warmth of him.

"I love you, Caro," he whispered.

"I love you, too." She pressed a kiss on the curve of his shoulder. It seemed a good place to put a kiss. Shoulders could be terribly neglected. She made a mental note of all the places on him she was never going to neglect. "Alan," she said softly, "I'm sorry. For you, and for your little Jonathan."

His arms tightened. "I never meant to take it out on you, kitten."

"You didn't," she assured him.

Both were sleepy, and both were certainly tired. The luminous dial on his bedside clock ticked one, then two. They were still talking. She'd known that he'd finished an internship in pediatric neurology once upon a time and only later opted to practice general pediatrics. She'd never known why he'd made that change. Now he told her. Neurologists had to treat hundreds of hopeless cases, too many little ones who couldn't make it. Objectivity was something he expected of himself, but had yet to achieve.

She listened, but heard more than he was telling her. Alan had never talked to her like this, never revealed his vulnerabilities, his lost dreams. Thoughts filtered through her mind . . . that he was far too hard on himself; she was going to have to work on that. That she could picture him so well as a father—pray God only that he'd settle for less than a dozen kids—but that he was really going to be Silly Putty around them. She and Alan were going to have extremely spoiled children. The thought delighted her.

And Alan listened, hearing stories of her growing up that he hadn't heard before, hearing more than the simple narratives. She came from a loving family; that was nothing he didn't know. But how often Carroll had assumed the role of peacemaker between her sister and mother—that he hadn't known. Suddenly, it was easy to understand why she'd adopted a practical, responsible role, keeping her dreams hidden. When they married, she was going to be free to dream, to be impulsive when she wanted to be. The thought delighted him.

Words grew softer, less frequent. "Sleepy?" he whispered.

She was, until she felt his palm on her spine, rubbing up and down, up and down, so soothing and gentle that there was no excuse at all for lightning suddenly to slash through her bloodstream. She reached for him.

In the morning, she woke up to the shock of sunlight. Alan was still sleeping, and she might have dozed off again if her eyes hadn't focused on her surroundings. Groggy lethargy abruptly disappeared.

This wasn't the room she remembered. They were sleeping on black satin sheets. His new spread was a zebra-striped fur. Wild African molas hung on the walls, all primitive slashes of color.

Good Lord.

Slowly, she snuggled back next to him. Alan, she thought humorously, I can take the Fiero, and I can take the beard if I have to, but honestly...

Unease wandered through her mind, the same unease that had been nagging her for weeks. A blind fool couldn't have missed the striking changes he'd made in his lifestyle. Carroll wasn't blind, but neither was she delighted by some of the new touches. Waking up to zebra stripes every morning, a steady diet of caviar and squid in hot tomato sauce—no, but darn it, she didn't want to hurt his feelings.

Never in her life had she imagined lovemaking as she'd experienced it the night before. Necking at the conference and roses and dancing all night—she'd love all of it, but what mattered was that they'd come together the night before naturally and with honest feelings. She'd never needed the roses. She *had* needed to know that he cared about her with honesty and depth . . . and that she was capable of feeling the same way. Alan had made that possible by opening himself up to her in the last few weeks.

That should have been the only thing that mattered, and it was. Except that a once-predictable man was becoming totally unpredictable. And security was nurtured by understanding . . . and there were times lately when she didn't understand him at all.

The man next to her suddenly showed remarkable energy for someone who was supposed to be sound asleep. He nuzzled her as he tugged her underneath him; he nuzzled her arms as he wrapped them around his neck; he nuzzled her lips until they parted, and he rubbed against her until her legs opened, too.

Oh, hell, she thought helplessly. If he really wanted to, he could decorate the whole place in zebra stripes.

It was the last thought she had for some time. Alan settled right down to the business of pleasure. Hers. If she'd had any last lingering doubts that he found her body beautiful, they rapidly disappeared. He liked everything. Breasts, ribs, wrists. Nose. Ears. Navel.

Nothing was off limits to the man, and he was incredibly slow. She did any number of clever things to speed him up, but he was clearly intent on driving her mad with wanting. She'd never been the kind of woman who could be driven mad with wanting.

Alan proved her wrong, and when it was over, she lay wrapped in his arms, too exhausted to lift a finger, too sated to move. "Don't," she murmured.

"Don't what?"

"You're looking at me," she accused him from behind closed eyes.

"I love looking at you. I'm never going to stop looking at you. Caro?"

"Hmmm?"

"You're a delicious lover. And a delectable woman. And I never even imagined loving anyone as much as I love you. And if I never told you before, I—*hey.*"

Her eyes shot open. She could feel the warm flush on her skin from his whispered words, but it wasn't that warm flush Alan was staring at. Glaring at, actually. His forefinger gently, softly touched the chafed skin around her breasts.

"Did I do that to you?" he demanded gruffly.

"Alan, it's nothing."

"My beard did that to you, and you never said one word?"

"It's nothing, honestly. The redness will go away. It doesn't hurt. It's nothing," she assured him, but he was already leaping out of bed, heading for the bathroom.

Fifteen minutes later, she had her clean-shaven man back again. When he pounced on the bed, he had a devilish gleam in his eye, and a lot of interest in rubbing his smooth cheeks in lots of sensitive places.

She could have sworn she didn't have an ounce of energy left in her body, but she miraculously found some. Her heart soared from kiss to kiss.

Those little nagging voices in her head ceased once and for all. Zebra stripes notwithstanding, no woman could be so foolish as to think anything was wrong with a man who loved like that.

Alan's mother had served a New England boiled dinner on Sundays for as long as he could remember. He'd hated it just about that long . . . but would probably have missed it if she stopped. Her kitchen hadn't changed since his childhood. Blue linoleum floors were waxed to a fine shine; pale cupboards gleamed with care; the old enamel teapot on the stove had always had the same chip. An ornate lamp stood in the center of the kitchen table. As a child, he'd been fascinated by its dangling glass prisms.

"Don't know as I like the President's stance at that summit meeting," his father said as he spooned a large helping of meat and potatoes onto his plate. Reed slim and bald as a cue ball, Stan expected his wife to interrupt them the minute she sat down, and she did.

"What's Carroll going to wear to her sister's wedding, Alan? Isn't it coming up next Saturday? *Stanley,* you've hogged all the potatoes again!"

"There are plenty of potatoes left."

"All that starch isn't good for you." Plump, with round blue eyes and curly bangs, Lucy clucked disapprovingly. "Isn't she maid of honor, Alan?"

"Isn't *who* maid of honor?" Stan demanded. "I tell you, Lucy, one of these years you're going to learn to stick to one question at a time."

At an early age, Alan had learned to get his conversational licks in when he could. Carrying on dialogues about weddings, summit meetings, and his medical practice all at once, he kept a shrewd eye on his mother's movements, knowing she had trouble with arthritis, and initiated a discussion on retirement with his dad. Stan had a year to go before he reached sixty-five, but unless he started to develop outside interests, he was going to drive himself and Lucy nuts wandering aimlessly around the house when that time came. Leopards didn't change their spots. Stan was a workaholic, but Alan was slowly, methodically working on him.

"Ready for big pearl tapioca, everyone?" His mother jumped up for the tenth time since the meal started.

"I can get it, Mom."

"Sit down, sit down. For heaven's sake, you'd think I was helpless. You know, Alan, I was hoping you might get a teensy-weensy little idea from this wedding . . ."

". . . So like you told me, I looked in the want ads and sure enough there was a lathe on sale. Hadn't worked with one of those since I was a kid. Made a pair of bookends for your mother . . . not that I'd take up woodworking as a full-time hobby, mind you."

"She's such a nice girl, already like one of the family. Not like that London woman you brought home a long time ago. And your father and I would never push you, Alan, but—"

". . . damn chisel broke right in my hands. They don't make things like these used to. Saw a sale down at Sears, though . . ."

". . . grandchildren . . ."

"Best tapioca you've ever made, Lucy."

His mother blushed bright pink, speechless. Stan said that to her every Sunday; it still seemed to astound her. Alan regarded his parents with warm affection, his thoughts about six and a half miles away and two streets down, give or take an apartment house.

He'd heard his mother's prompting. He didn't need it. A simple gold band had been on his mind since he met Carroll, but then last night . . . she'd been so free in loving. Wild and giving and wanton, her face flushed with passion, her eyes shimmering with it, her skin quivering when he touched her just so . . .

He'd had in mind everything perfect for the first time, an orchestration of romantic fantasy—not an unplanned coming together that a tidal wave couldn't have stopped.

Truthfully, he was relieved it had happened so naturally, but their lovemaking had also confirmed what he already knew. Freedom and passion and excitement and the surprise of the unexpected were what a woman wanted in a man, what Carroll wanted and needed.

"Neither of you want another helping of tapioca?" Lucy asked disappointedly.

"Mom, we've already had two."

"Can't have enough of a good thing."

True, Alan thought fleetingly.

She loved him. He hadn't been positive that anything he'd done had made a difference until last night. Now he knew, and he wasn't about to blow it, or coast just because he'd crossed a few hurdles.

Marriage meant settling down. He simply had to stop himself from thinking on those terms, no matter how hard it was. The excitement of a lover and a love affair were what clearly appealed to her.

Dammit, he had to find some way to give her that. His previous efforts had been paltry. Anything was possible now that he knew she loved him back. No way he was going back to being stodgy.

Chapter 9

"WONDERFUL WEDDING! ABSOLUTELY wonderful!" Mrs. Tobins leaned close to buss Carroll's cheek, and whispered, "I don't doubt for a minute you'll be next, darling! Don't you worry about a thing. You'll land that young man of yours!"

Carroll smiled, a little wanly. Who could have guessed that the receiving line would be a gauntlet? Her feet were killing her; she was so tired she could have fallen asleep standing on her head; and if one more person made one more reference to her single state . . .

George Brooks stepped forward next, pumped her hand like the healthy man he was, and leaned his florid face toward her. "You always were twice as pretty as your sis," he boomed. "Be at the altar yourself within a year, gal. And if your beau don't have that kind of sense, I'll divorce my Marabelle and marry you myself."

A fate worse than death, Carroll thought dryly. Not that her mother's longtime neighbor wasn't trying to be kind. "Thanks so much, George." All right. If *one* more person made *one* more comment . . .

Mary Sue Stuart loomed next in the receiving line, herding her second husband and three children ahead of her. "Sweetie, when on earth are you going to pin down that adorable doctor?" she whispered, with the exact same giggle that had driven Carroll nuts since they were in grade school.

She hardly had the option to scream, and once the receiving line ended, she could get off her feet for only a few short minutes. Maybe she was becoming inordinately touchy on the subject of Alan and marriage. A little break was all she needed . . . but breaks were in short supply for the next hour and a half.

Once the wedding guests had been greeted, the reception dinner began. Carroll, stuck at the head table as maid of honor, kept trying to sneak glimpses of Alan . . . but Alan seemed inordinately busy with the tipsy blonde in gold brocade at the third table.

Following dinner, the band started to play. Stéphane led Nancy in the traditional first dance, after which the bridegroom came toward Carroll to claim the second. *No,* she thought fleetingly, *my feet really aren't capable of moving* . . . but there was no help for it. With a brilliant smile, she let Stéphane lead her to the dance floor.

"How's my newest sister tonight . . . besides breathtakingly beautiful?"

"Nowhere near as resplendent as my new brother," she responded lightly, and tried to relax in his arms. Stéphane, in white tie and cutaway, looked like a storybook prince and danced like Baryshnikov. Neither of those things surprised her, but discovering that she genuinely liked her new brother-in-law did. He *was* a charmer; it wasn't fake.

As far as his compliment went, she might not be "breathtaking," but Carroll definitely felt beautiful.

Her gown was apricot velvet, with a deeply scooped neckline and long sleeves that ended in delicate points at her wrists. Rapunzel might have worn this dress. Sleeping beauty. Cinderella. But only Nance would have been imaginative enough to pick it out for her maid of honor.

She felt almost like a beauty . . . but a beauty very close to total collapse. It might be only nine in the evening, but the day had been hectic—not to mention the week leading up to it. Her feet were still killing her, her head was pounding, and her vision was blurred from lack of sleep.

She didn't want to see another dance floor, another magnum of champagne, or another flower for the next hundred years, give or take a few.

On Monday, Alan had picked her up after work, and they'd driven to a nightclub in Chicago. She'd drunk far too much champagne, danced her feet off altogether, and arrived home in time to snatch three hours of rest before going to work the next day. On Tuesday, he'd arrived with his arms full of flowers and tickets to a mime production at the university. On Wednesday, he'd brought her gardenias and led her into the woods, where he'd cooked dinner over an open fire, then taken her home to Cold Duck and candlelight. On Thursday, he'd found an all-weather skating rink that played romantic music until the wee hours.

Last night had been the rehearsal dinner, which had ended early enough, if either of them had had the sense to just go home and go to bed. They'd gone home. And gone to bed. They just hadn't slept.

Sometime soon, she had to sleep. All the razzle-dazzle was delightful; she felt courted like a princess. Only at the ragged old age of twenty-seven, she was starting to get dark circles under her eyes, and the wedding—to her own surprise—was making her a little nervous. Courting usually led to a ring. Alan hadn't mentioned rings in weeks.

Finally, the dance ended . . . and before the band could begin another song, the guests began clinking spoons against their glasses, demanding in the traditional way that the groom kiss the bride. Stéphane winked a good-bye at her, and went off in search of Nancy. The crystal-metal clanging had reached fever pitch by the time the two obediently pleased the crowd by going into a passionate clinch.

Watching them, the silliest blur filled Carroll's eyes. How sentimental could you get? And it had started for her at the church, when she'd seen the reflection of candlelight on stained glass, heard the first strains of the wedding march, and sensed the promise of love in the air.

Turning, she saw Alan coming toward her across the crowded room and immediately moved toward him. He was lost from sight for a minute, and she stole one last glance at her brother-in-law. Stéphane was just as tall, dark, and handsome as she'd first thought, just as sexy, his smile just as roguish.

Her eyes flickered immediately back to Alan. His dark suit was new and stylishly tailored and his linen shirt impeccable, but some things hadn't changed. His diagonal tie was askew, his hair just a little rumpled, his collar just a little too tight. It didn't matter.

As he neared, her heart beat faster all at once. Her skin warmed, her toes tingled, her eyes softened. There was really no comparison between the two men. Stéphane was just your average swashbuckling hero type.

Alan was Alan.

He reached her and held out his hands. She clasped them, smiling. "Can I steal you away from family responsibilities just for a minute?" he said teasingly.

"Instantly," she assured him.

"Good." With an arm at her waist, he steered her toward the door.

Outside, the night air was close to freezing, but the cold felt good after being surrounded by too many people and too much smoke for so many hours. "I told myself I was going to wait to give you this until the end of the evening, Caro . . . but I couldn't wait."

Her lips parted in surprise as he plucked a small velvet box from his pocket, and then she just looked at him. Love filled her eyes like the sheen of stars. "Oh, Alan . . ."

"Open it, love."

Her silly fingers were trembling, but she managed to part the stiff catch of the box. The yard light was brilliant, easily bright enough for her to see its contents—a ruby heart strung on the most fragile braided gold chain she'd ever laid eyes on. For a moment, she couldn't say a thing for the lump in her throat.

The gift was exquisite . . . but not what she was expecting.

"Like it?"

"It's beautiful. The most beautiful thing I've ever seen," she murmured truthfully. "I adore it, Alan."

"Let me put it on for you."

She obediently turned and closed her eyes as she felt his gentle hands fasten the clasp at the nape of her neck. Love swirled through her on about an equal level with despair. Her eyes stayed closed until she was absolutely positive she wasn't going to cry.

Oh, my darling, I love it, adore it, cherish it, can't believe you did this, and will never in a hundred years forget to appreciate you, but . . .

Dammit, Alan, where's my ring?

"Squish squish squish . . . getting the idea, Tiger?"

The five-year-old's name was Aaron Barkman, and Carroll hadn't figured out yet who'd thought Tiger was an appropriate nickname. To her, Tiger suggested a physical child who liked a little romp and stomp and noise.

Aaron was wearing a button-down shirt, white vest, neatly creased jeans, and unscuffed shoes. She'd talked him into putting a smock over his clothes, but as yet the smock hadn't seen a smudge of paint. Standing with his arms folded, his serious brown eyes fixed on the finger paint she was mixing as if he were watching a monkey in the zoo . . . and being patient about it. "My mother said I was here to work," he remarked gravely.

"We *are* working. Come on, try it."

He sighed like a tired little ninety-year-old man, and cautiously edged closer. "It's a very nice picture," he said politely.

Carroll dearly wished she could get the child away from his mother for a full twenty-four hours, preferably near a mud puddle on a hot day. "Come on. Get your fingers in it. Squish it all up!"

"You're going to tell my mother we've been working?"

"I certainly am."

"It'll get under my fingernails."

"Your hands'll wash. I guarantee it."

In time, he was persuaded to mix blue and red. A little later, he was persuaded to paint letters and sound them out. With older children, the technique didn't work, but Carroll, because she'd been well trained, knew that hearing and sight often needed to be combined with the sense of touch in teaching young children. If they made the letters—preferably in their favorite color—as they were sounding them out, somehow they began to understand what had previously been a mystery to them.

The finger paintings were drying a half-hour later. Having washed his hands and put away his smock, Aaron put on his coat and then gravely extended his hand. Carroll shook it with equal gravity. "I'll come back and work some more with you this afternoon, if you want," Aaron offered seriously. "But I think you'd do better if I did the mixing."

"You think I'm a little messy?"

He nodded. "My mother would die."

When he was gone, thoroughly disappointed that he couldn't return until next week, Carroll tugged down her yellow sweater and grinned. She'd give him a few more weeks to get used to her before she scared him to bits with a giant bear hug.

Her stomach growled, and she glanced at the clock. Hungry or not, in the half-hour before lunch she had in mind cramming in three hours of paperwork. She was stapling dittoed papers together on the red carpet when she heard a "Pssst" from the door. Glancing up, she felt her lips curl in an immediate smile. "Alan! Surely you're not here to sit through *another* three hours of *s*'s and *l*'s!"

Alan chuckled, shaking his head. "Where's your coat?"

"You're taking me out to lunch?" she asked.

She hurried, belting her cherry wool coat, and grabbed her purse. A long morning had just been given a lift, and she hadn't seen Alan since the night of the wedding.

Memories of that night rushed back to her. She'd been so disappointed that he hadn't given her a ring. Between that and a zombielike case of tiredness, she really hadn't been "in the mood" when Alan had taken her home. But then, she hadn't planned on Alan's using his diagonal-striped tie to blindfold her en route to seducing her.

Shortly thereafter, she'd forgotten tiredness and forgotten rings. Alan had been simply, gently, and tenderly determined to bring out the abandoned woman in her. He'd certainly succeeded. So often she used the sense of touch as a teaching tool for her little ones. She'd never considered how it would feel to have the tables turned on her. While she was deprived of sight, her sense of touch had been exquisitely intensified, until their lovemaking had become an explosion of tactile explorations and feelings . . .

Really, Alan was becoming the most demanding lover.

And his surprise appearance at lunchtime was simply a joy. "I'm starving," she confessed as she lifted the purse strap to her shoulder. Alan pushed open the door so she could walk out ahead of him. "It's snowing."

"Yes."

The sky was alive with little flakes, more like gently tossed confetti than serious snow. She stood patiently while Alan insisted on adjusting her scarf. It was an excuse to touch her, nothing more. For an instant, blue eyes met brown, nothing planned, nothing intentional, and the next thing she knew his arms were around her and they were kissing. And shivering.

Alan pulled back, a sparkle in his eyes that boded ill for her sanity, and grabbed her hand.

"Where we going? Apple Annie's?"

"Nope."

"Bruno's?"

"We're going somewhere you never dreamed you'd be taken to lunch. No more questions." He closed the passenger door.

"Pizza?" she quizzed the minute he opened his door. "Burgers? Soup and salad?"

"It's in the female genes," Alan said to the windshield.

"What is?"

"Curiosity. You'll see soon enough, Caro."

She saw soon enough that he was turning into the Sheraton Inn's parking lot. Her eyebrows lifted as she sneaked a look at him. The Sheraton put on a pretty fancy lunch for two people who usually hit and ran a quick-lunch stop between working hours.

Alan, she just noticed, was looking vaguely like a ten-year-old gloating over a secret. On the surface, of course, the image was one of a successful doctor. His pants were freshly creased, the camel suit one of his old ones—conservative and tasteful. With the beard gone, he had a clean, distinguished profile. Alan had a natural dignity, she decided absently.

She couldn't imagine why the picture of a gloating ten-year-old persisted.

She glanced in the rearview mirror, becoming aware he was driving past the restaurant parking area toward the inn's back lot, making for an unnecessarily long walk. There were several spaces close to the restaurant door, and it was cold outside. "Did you miss the parking space next to that truck?" she asked lightly.

"We can go in the back way. You won't be cold," he promised her.

And she wasn't. Seconds later, they were both out of the chill and striding down the long corridor of the rear entrance to the inn. A maid was pushing a cleaning cart down the hall. Slightly unsure of the route back to the restaurant, Carroll turned to Alan. About that instant, he captured her arm.

She caught the strange glitter of a gold key in his hand, but it didn't really register until he fitted it in the door. When he gently pushed her a step backward, her lips parted in surprise. Darkness. Though the day was brightly lit, blackout drapes sealed the darkness in. When the door closed behind Alan, for a moment she could see nothing.

"Al—?"

His lips sealed hers, the kiss of a kidnapper, a pirate. Her coat was pushed off, landed in a woosh at
her feet. Her arms seemed to be hanging in midair,
too startled to know what to do with themselves.
Then they were over her head, as Alan pulled off her
yellow sweater. It must have hit a lamp shade,
because she heard something rocking back and forth.
Her bra went in the direction of the door. Her brown
slacks slid down over her hips and were hurled somewhere, making hangers clatter together in a most
abandoned way.

Removing pantyhose took two hands. In this case,
it took two hands and a mouth. Alan kissed each inch
of her as he peeled the nylon down. Her knees buck-
led. A smooth, cool bed was right there to take care
of that problem, except that the coolness was another
problem. She seemed to be shivering everywhere,
inside her toes, on the surface of her skin, in her ears,
her brain, her fingertips.

Her kidnapper did nothing to help her. Her kidnapper seemed to have several pairs of hands,
because while Brooks Brothers garments were hitting
the floor, a set of hands never abandoned her. Kisses
landed indiscriminately on breast, navel, thigh.

A half-hour before, her mind had been on speech,
an urchin named Aaron, the appeasement of a growl-
ing stomach. She was a responsible woman in the
middle of a workday. That was sanity.

This was the shadow of a man in darkness, the
naughtiness of a motel room, the danger in knowing

there were people passing just outside the door, their
voices raised in normal conversation. "You're
craz—" she started to say, but his mouth molded on
hers. She tasted mint, warm wetness, the flavor of
desire.

"Open for me," he whispered. "Now, Caro."

Her legs wrapped around him, sealing him inside
her. A whirlwind of darkness swirled in front of her
eyes. She could hear the beat of her heart, feel the
beat of his. His breath was fierce, harsh. She wasn't
sure if she was breathing at all, but her skin was
suddenly as hot as fire, as delicate as a cotton puff.

Energy flowed through her in a lambent rush, a
slick, lazy, powerful energy. She felt . . . taken. Taken
with fierce, sharp strokes, possessive strokes, I'm-
going-to-have-you, no-more-talk strokes. Wicked,
wild speed. She marveled at what he could make her
feel, do, think, want, need. A man in love had so
much power.

A woman in love had so much more.

An hour later, the doors to the school clicked shut
behind her. Carroll glanced quickly at her watch, and
stumbled. A minute after one. She unbuttoned her
coat as she hurried down the corridor, empty as
classes were just beginning, and tripped again. With
a frown, she looked down at her legs as if they
belonged to a stranger. *Look, we learned to walk at a
year old. Do you think we could manage to
remember the basic procedure?*

"Carroll?" Mrs. Williamson, the school secretary,
rushed toward her. "About those evaluations Mr.

McCarthy wanted to discuss with you on the new students? He wondered if you had a few minutes to spare now instead of at two."

"No problem—just give me a second to get rid of my coat." She hung it in her classroom, and grabbed her brush and a small mirror from her purse.

Her reflection startled her. Her cheeks had color that didn't come from the cold day outside. Her brown eyes had an unforgivable sleepy glaze. Her lips looked carmine, and she wasn't wearing a speck of lipstick. And she didn't need to look down to know her legs were still wobbly.

You have an appointment with the principal, she reminded that face. *Shape up.*

Her stomach growled. A sign of normalcy, but not much of one. She could still feel the slight dampness between her legs, still imagine the texture of his lips against her breasts. The flush on her face deepened.

"Carroll, Mr. McCarthy—" The secretary was at her door again, this time looking frantic.

"Yes," she said. She was in the school, she tried to remind herself. She had to remember—immediately —exactly why she had a meeting with the principal. She had to remember how to walk in a straight line.

Impossible, on all accounts.

Never, ever in her life had she imagined a man who loved her enough, wanted her enough, needed her enough to throw caution and common sense to the winds . . . and to make her do it, too.

But enough, Alan, her heart whispered. For a lifetime, she was willing to explore sexual adventures with him. She was just becoming increasingly frightened because he wasn't mentioning lifetimes.

After all this time, did he really want nothing more than an affair?

Friday night, seated at her kitchen table, Alan looked innocently unaware of the trap Carroll had set for him.

It didn't look like much of a trap, but then, that was the point. She'd served him ordinary beer as an apperitif, something he used to like before he got into tequila and champagne. She'd urged him to wear jeans and a sweat shirt—the kind of clothes they used to relax in after a hard week's work. The menu included no Spanish, Hungarian, or Tibetan delicacies. In fact, she'd whipped up a simple meat loaf and mashed potatoes, something he used to like before he got into cactus paddles.

Having set such a clever trap, she only wished she knew what it was for. All she wanted to do was talk to Alan after dinner, seriously talk. And somehow she hoped that would be easier if Alan hadn't changed quite as totally as she was afraid he'd changed.

Even so, she was both relieved and startled at Alan's reaction to the meal. He took one look, enthused, "Looks terrific!" and plunged in as if he'd just ended a four-week fast. More slowly, she settled in the chair across from him and passed a plate of steaming blueberry muffins.

"Caro, I'm going to weigh three hundred pounds after this meal," he scolded.

"Devil's food cake with chocolate frosting for dessert."

He looked at her with the expression of a man who enjoyed pain. She giggled, and then it most oddly occurred to her that she hadn't simply giggled around him in weeks. "So tell me again what else the woman said," she said.

He shook his head. "I still don't believe it. Here are her three kids sitting side by side on the examining table, absolutely peppered with chicken pox— Carroll, do *not* let me have another muffin—and she's wondering if there's a little rash going around. It never once occurred to her to let the school know —all right, Caro, one more, but absolutely *none* after that—and you realize what this means for the next six weeks? Parents panicking and the schools worrying about epidemics . . ." He looked up suddenly. "You've had chicken pox, haven't you?"

"Ages ago."

"Still, in rare instances, it strikes the same person twice, so it isn't wise to expose yourself to it. Take an extra good look at your urchins before you start drilling those *l*'s and *s*'s."

"Just like you'll be extra careful with the kids parading in and out of your office?"

"It's not the same thing," he said firmly.

She rose, picked up their empty plates, and paused to kiss him on the nape of his neck. He smelled like a fresh shower, like a bracing soap and a man's shampoo. She was vaguely aware he'd forgotten his sandalwood and musk, and was even more vaguely aware that she was glad. "It's *exactly* the same thing."

"Come back here and do that again when you're within grabbing distance."

She brandished the cake on a blue Wedgewood plate in front of him. "This is a test," she announced. "You can grab either me or the cake."

"Do I fail the test if I take the cake now and grab you later?"

"Men," Carroll told the cake as she cut it, "are all alike. Here all this time I thought he loved me for myself, when all along . . ."

It was tough eating the cake while she was pinned on Alan's lap. He fed her pieces that were far too large, then licked the crumbs from her chin, then managed to steal bites from her plate. He also stole chocolate-flavored kisses.

And the whole time she was laughing, she was trying to find the right words to say. She didn't want to hurt him. She didn't want to destroy the relationship they had together.

She was just increasingly afraid that if she didn't say something soon, she was going to end up living in a barn with a man who wasn't her husband. That the place was going to be decorated in zebra stripes, sports cars were going to line the driveway, and out-of-wedlock children were going to be raised on cactus paddles and quail in thyme sauce.

"Alan?" she said finally.

He found yet another crumb on her chin and flicked it off with the pad of his thumb, following this up with a kiss. "Did I tell you I got tickets to the ballet in Chicago for next Tuesday?"

"Ballet?" She laughed because, darn it, his nuzzling was tickling her, but the thought of another week of late nights made her feel exhausted before it had even started. "Alan, you *hate* the ballet."

"I love you, sweet."

"And I love you, but that's exactly what I'd like to talk to you about—ballets and nightclubs and dancing and . . ." She took a breath and tried to make her tone sound teasing, casual. "Alan, you know, there was a time when I thought you seriously disliked all those things—"

For an instant, she was sure she saw a flash of bright blue guilt in eyes, but then it was gone, and Alan was suddenly talking fast and low as he teased the shell of her ear. "Nonsense. I love nothing better than doing exciting things with you, sweet—and we have to go dancing again. Someplace quieter this time. With soft lights and a postage stamp–size dance floor where I can hold you closer than you should be held in public, and you can drink just a little too much champagne."

"Alan—"

"You can get very silly when you drink too much champagne."

"I know I can. But—"

The phone jangled. She looked helplessly at Alan before sliding off his lap to answer it. Running a hand through her hair, she snapped an abrupt hello into the phone, then realized it was his answering service. "For you."

It wasn't the first time he'd left her number, and she knew well what a call in the evening meant. Still . . . she was the one who should have been upset. Instead, Alan leaped out of the chair as if his fanny had just connected with tacks, and alarm put a frantic glint in his eyes. "Don't worry. I'm *not* leaving tonight," he promised her as he took the phone.

No? Heart sinking, she started collecting the dessert dishes.

"Randy Jenkins," he said when he hung up a few moments later. "I know darn well it's just another case of chicken pox, which I told his mother——"

"Alan, it's all right," she said soothingly as she fetched his coat. It wasn't all right, exactly, but their talk would just have to wait. One didn't date a pediatrician without knowing the pitfalls, and whining about spilled milk never put it back in the pail.

"Caro, I can't leave *now*."

She raised a quizzical eyebrow. "You can come back here right afterward, can't you? And you know I understand."

"Believe me, honey, you *don't* understand," he said heavily, and raked a hand through his hair. "Maybe I could call Mrs. Jenkins back."

They both knew he wasn't calling Mrs. Jenkins back, and that he was leaving. Even if the boy only had a hangnail, Alan would worry about him until he saw for himself that the child wasn't seriously ill. She wasn't at all surprised to see Alan suddenly jam his arms into his coatsleeves and grab his keys, but she *was* surprised that he was so upset about something he obviously couldn't help. "I'll be back absolutely as fast I can. I *promise*," he said heatedly.

"Alan, is something wrong?"

"Nothing, absolutely nothing. Just don't leave here, okay? Promise me, Caro."

"Fine." She couldn't keep the bewilderment out of her tone, and then he was gone.

Chapter 10

SHAKING HER HEAD, Carroll closed the door. After she finished the dishes, she flopped on the couch with a book, but her mind was still on Alan's strange behavior.

She tried for an hour but couldn't concentrate on the mystery in her hands. Every time she glanced up, she saw flowers. Gardenias spilled out of their vases on the mantel; daffodils were starting to droop over her coffee table; the fresh roses he'd brought yesterday filled every spare nook and cranny.

Her apartment smelled like a cross between a country garden and a funeral parlor, and the look of all those flowers suddenly brought on an anxiety attack. Snapping the book closed, Carroll sprang to her feet, stuck her hands in the back pockets of her jeans, and starting pacing.

She'd been pretty selfish.

Or blind. For weeks, Alan had been sending flowers, taking her places, doing things—and for all those weeks she'd quietly accepted those attentions and blithely taken them as signs of love from Alan. They *were* signs of love, she mentally reassured herself, only maybe she'd been eagerly picking up those signals and ignoring others.

Was she losing him?

Had he been trying to tell her that he was bored at the thought of quiet evenings at home with her? That he'd never valued the comfortable little talks they used to have? That he did love her in a certain way, but not in a way that included children and swing sets and a station wagon and . . . well . . . a lifetime?

Maybe he'd always wanted a more exciting woman. Maybe he'd done all those things because he wanted her to be a different kind of person. Maybe he'd kidded himself into believing she *was* different —that she thrived on dancing all night and receiving flowers, and that she had dozens of adventurous fantasies like canoeing at midnight. Maybe he wanted a woman to climb into *his* bedroom in the wee hours?

And darn it, she supposed she could do something like that if it would really please Alan, but it wasn't the point. The point was that maybe she'd kidded herself into believing she was the right woman for him.

Feeling gloomy and low, Carroll stopped pacing and curled up in a chair, desperately wishing she had answers. She needed to concentrate . . . and concentration became more and more difficult because of the haunting sounds coming from her back courtyard. Guitars?

Obviously, the wind. Frowning, Carroll rubbed two fingers on her temples and tried to think . . . but the throb of guitars persisted.

Irritably, she stood up and stalked through her kitchen to peer through the window over the sink. Her jaw dropped in surprise. Four men stood outside in the courtyard, dressed in black and wearing sombreros. They were looking at *her,* and the minute they made eye contact they bowed their respects.

Lights blinked on all over the apartment complex, and her throat was suddenly dry as she threw open the window. The musicians, nodding and smiling, sauntered toward her and stood in a semicircle looking up at her, never missing a note. She didn't know the name of the song, but it was distinctly Spanish, romantic, and soulful. Wrapping her arms around herself against the frigid night air, she tried to look appreciative. Oh, Alan, she thought helplessly.

When the song ended, she enthusiastically applauded and called out her thanks, praying that would be the end of the serenade . . . but the guitarists immediately burst into a wild flamenco number. Inside the apartment, she heard the jangle of her telephone. Making an apologetic motion to the musicians, she rushed to answer it, combing her hair distractedly with her fingers.

"No, Mr. Bartholomew. Honestly, I had no idea. I'm sorry they were disturbing you . . ."

She returned to a tango. She tried to explain in sign language that as much as she loved their music, she wanted them to stop, but one of the men kept shaking his head, smiling at her, calling out about how romance and love and music were everything.

Again the phone rang and, cheeks blotched red, Carroll rushed back inside. "Mrs. Roberts, I'm terribly sorry you were asleep. Yes, I know you work an early-morning shift even on Saturdays . . ."

The serenaders left a half-hour later. Carroll had barely locked the door and flicked off the light before she heard a rapid knock at the front door. She flew to answer it, expecting Alan and not at all sure what she was going to say to him.

No pediatrician stood on her doorstep. The two strange men were dressed in blue, wore hip holsters, and looked official. "Is this the place that had the outdoor music?" the steel-haired one demanded.

"I . . . yes, but—"

"We've had a complaint, miss."

Just about then, she wished she'd simply die and go to heaven. Or hell. It didn't make much difference. The officers were mollified with promises it would never happen again. Actually, they were highly amused by the entire incident.

Carroll wasn't. She *wanted* to feel charmed, but this time it just wasn't working. And it occurred to her that for weeks now, she'd only been *trying* to feel charmed by many of Alan's romantic gestures. After all, what kind of woman got depressed over the gift of a ruby heart?

Her kind of woman, she thought miserably. She'd never wanted rubies or serenades. Just Alan. The Alan she'd thought she had.

She was sitting by the phone when he rang at midnight. His sober voice immediately squelched the first words she'd planned to say to him. "I'm sorry I couldn't get back to you sooner, Caro. It wasn't another case of chicken pox. I'm with Randy's parents at the hospital—he has hepatitis."

A dozen emotions were quickly shelved. "Oh, honey. He'll be all right?"

"In time, yes, and he's resting now—but, Caro, I'm likely to be here for another hour. Just go to sleep, would you, kitten? And I'll see you in the morning."

"Yes," she agreed. And while she took a huge breath, there was a nervous cough on the other end of the line, then a second one. In the process of clearing his voice, Alan's exhausted, grave tone was miraculously replaced by one of boyish shyness.

"Anything . . . unusual . . . happen tonight?" he asked casually.

She lifted the phone from her ear and stared at it. *Alan,* she thought wearily, *enough really is . . . enough.*

Bone tired, Alan pushed off the lights and climbed out of his car. Not a sound or movement disturbed the quiet street at this late hour. Jamming his hands in his pockets, head down against the cold, he aimed for his apartment door.

His memory was being buffeted by the smells of antiseptics, and Carroll. Of the look of a little boy finally peacefully sleeping in a hospital bed, and Carroll. Of parents too frightened to be rational, and Carroll. And the last thing he expected to find on climbing the three steps up to his door was . . . Carroll, a scarf wrapped around her throat and a white angora hat pulled low over her forehead.

He stopped dead, his heart pumping panic to every nerve ending. "Good Lord, what's wrong? You haven't been standing out here in this cold for lo—"

"I had to talk to you, and it wouldn't wait," she said crisply. "The child's all right, Alan?"

"Randy—yes. I . . ." He fumbled with his apartment key, and then hustled her inside ahead of him.

While he stood in the hallway removing his jacket, she moved inside, switching on lamps and tugging off her hat and scarf. But he couldn't miss noting, when she perched on the edge of the couch, that she hadn't taken off her coat.

She didn't intend to stay. Anxiety hit his gut with all the delicacy of a Mack truck. "What's wrong?"

"A great deal, I'm afraid," she said quietly.

He tried, fast, to find a light note. "They were flat?" he said wryly.

"The serenaders were perfectly in tune, Alan. It's you and I who don't seem to be." She added softly, "I know you're tired. If you'd like me to make a pot of coffee—"

"No." Coffee wouldn't help. In fact, the smoothest of liquids probably couldn't push past the total dryness in his throat.

He'd been so sure it was working . . . and he'd come as close to being a romantic hero as he could. He thought she liked the new Alan. He'd liked some parts of the new image himself, but there wasn't a chance he could keep up the game for the next ninety years—even if he could stomach the food he'd been cooking, even if he could live with the impractical Fiero, even if he could manage to stay up night after night and still do a decent day's work the next day.

Which left Carroll loving a man he wasn't. Or not loving the man he was. Or in the worst possible scenario, the one twisting in his gut, Carroll not loving him at all.

"Please sit down, would you?" He was just standing there, staring at her with those fathomless, gentle blue eyes of his. She sprang from the couch, as rest-

less as a cat in a rainstorm and twice as miserable. She already knew she was going to make mess of this. She could never say things well when she was upset, and she was unquestionably upset. Her stomach was in knots, and her palms were damp, and her heart was beating erratically...because anxiety always made her heart beat erratically.

"Just say it, honey." Alan's voice was low.

She waved her hand helplessly, as if that could help her get the words out. "I thought...I *always* thought...I could be honest with you. From the day I met you, I thought we were capable of a special kind of honesty between us. Even from the very beginning, we could talk to each other—"

"We could and we can, Caro."

She shook her head. "I don't think so. I think I've been lying to you and you've been lying to me and—"

"I've never lied to you!" Alan said swiftly.

"No?" Her eyes were suddenly smarting with tears. "Then will you answer a few questions for me —with total honesty?"

His lungs released a sudden rush of air. She was at least talking—and not walking out. "Of course."

"They're really very simple questions." Sticking her hands in her coat pockets, she tried to smile, and almost did. "For a Sunday dinner," she said softly, "would you rather have a rib roast or squid in tomato sauce?"

Expecting the world to fall in, Alan wasn't at all prepared for the irrelevant question. "What?"

"You heard me."

"Rib roast. Carroll. Dammit, if you didn't like the

serenade, just say so. I can see it was a stupid idea. Forget it and let's just—"

"Do you like dancing, Alan?"

"I—sometimes." He couldn't take his eyes off her white face.

"You promised to be honest."

"*Sometimes* I like dancing. Caro—"

"And ballet? And nightclubs? And you really like sleeping on black satin sheets? You don't find them . . . slippery? And the wild zebra spread, Alan, tell me how you picked that out because it suited you."

He felt cornered at the end of a long corridor. "Sweetheart," he said in a low voice, "maybe I'm not quite so fond of those things as I let on, but—"

"I think you hate all of them," she said sadly. "And I finally figured out why you did all those things, Alan, why you've been lying to me." She took a long breath. "You were tired of me, weren't you? You wanted an affair, not marriage, not quiet evenings at home. The thing is, it would have been so much less painful if you'd just *told* me what you were feeling, that you really wanted and needed a very different kind of woman than I am. Because, Alan, I'm not—"

Talking was proving to be a terrible idea. Holing up in a corner to lick her wounds was a better one, much less humiliating. She made the three swift steps to the door before Alan sprang in front of her, his face gray with pain and his voice impossibly gentle. "You are so dead wrong, kitten."

She shook her head wildly, refusing to look at him. "I don't think so. Suddenly, we're having this affair. Suddenly, it's all different." She swiped at her eyes impatiently. "I think you always knew I wanted kids more than serenades. Station wagons, not Fieros. And even the barn, Alan. It could probably be a terrific home for someone, something unusual and unique and tremendously innovative and creative . . . but I never saw anything that wrong with a colonial house. With a standard old white picket fence—I just can't lie, Alan. I *like* white picket fences. I've always liked white—"

"God, I love you."

That was a perfectly awful thing to say, because it made tears gush from her eyes as if a dike had suddenly become unplugged. And Alan took most unfair advantage of her tears by moving forward, talking as he untangled the scarf from her hands, talking as he brushed the tears from her cheeks, talking as he firmly, gently started unbuttoning her coat. "I love you . . . so much. And I did everything, Caro, *everything* because I was afraid of losing you. I was trying to be . . . the man you needed in your life. The best way I knew how."

She didn't want to look at him, but his palms cupped her face, forcing her eyes to meet his. Even through a rainbow haze of tears, she could see the expression of the man she'd fallen in love with. A man she'd once believed would never lie to her . . . and whose sincerity was there now, in clear dark eyes, in a mouth rigid with anxiety, in the beat of the pulse in his temples. The fear in her heart eased, just a little. "But you were *always* that man. You never had to . . . make up things, or pretend, or . . ."

"But I did, Caro." He took her hand, led her to the couch, and doused the light that was glaring in her eyes when she sank down. "Weeks ago," he said gently, "I wanted to ask you to marry me. I didn't because I was afraid you'd say no—and it's your turn to be honest this time, kitten. You would have said no, wouldn't you?"

Her lips parted to instantly deny that . . . but then she couldn't, not when she remembered back to the way she'd felt at the time. And before she could stop him, he reached up gently, soothingly, to brush the last of the tears from her cheeks.

"If you'd had the right feelings," he said softly, "you wouldn't have held me off from sleeping with you. You felt warmth—a part of love. But not all I wanted from you, and not all I wanted for you."

She was suddenly staring at the wall, anywhere but at him. "But that was all a problem in me, Alan, not you," she said painfully.

"No," Alan insisted. "I know better, and I think you do, too. Maybe I'd lived alone too long, and maybe anyone who lives alone gets set in his ways, used to habits, lazy about thinking of other people's feelings. Those are the excuses, Caro, but the fact is that I was a die-hard fuddy-duddy in the making."

"Alan!" He heard the protest, and also caught the first hint of an unwilling smile on her lips. "You foolish man," she scolded, "you were never—"

"Oh, yes I was. *Not* a man who could keep your interest for the next ninety years and, just maybe, not someone I much wanted to be for the next ninety years, either." His tone softened. "If I went too far, you have to understand that I was starting from scratch. A blank piece of paper. Because I'd never wanted a woman half as much as I wanted you."

"Oh, Alan." She sank against his chest, felt his arms wrap around her as if she were coming home. "I had no idea how you felt. And I never loved you for the razzle-dazzle. I loved you for you. How could you think otherwise?"

His lips pressed into her hair. "What I think," he said honestly, "is that you needed the roses. That you were entitled to the roses. You wanted to *feel* loved, Caro, not just *be* loved. And *I* needed to feel that I could offer you something special. Not necessarily bizarre foods for dinner or canoe rides at midnight, but something you felt only when you were with me. The freedom to reach for your fantasies and make them real. Maybe just the freedom to be vulnerable. And honest. The freedom to express . . ." He ran out of words.

Carroll wanted to say that she'd been haunted by the same fears, that for a long time she'd worried that she didn't have anything special enough to offer him, that he was the one who had given her confidence in herself as a woman . . . In time she *would* tell him in elaborate detail, but perhaps not at the moment. Now it seemed the best of times to make sure that *he* felt loved, too, exactly as he'd made her feel loved.

"Freedom to be vulnerable," she murmured, and leaned back, studying the love in his eyes, breathing it, savoring it, feeling her heart well with it. "You know what you did to me, don't you, Alan?" she questioned gently. "You stole every inhibition I had, made me tell you every secret, made very sure I knew I was a passionate woman. You *forced* me to feel special, love . . . and I'm afraid you'll have to pay the price now."

"The pr—"

"No more talking," she scolded. "You're in a lot of trouble with me. You beguiled an awful lot of secrets out of me with your seductive tricks." She cast him a suddenly critical glance. "You look exhausted. Actually, you look like hell."

"What?"

The poor man looked dazed. She pressed a forefinger lightly against his chest, which shouldn't have been enough to force him down, but he went down, spine flat against the couch cushions.

"In the beginning," she said firmly, "maybe we *didn't* have the right kind of relationship. Maybe it took some changes to make it right. And maybe it still isn't exactly right, Alan, because it takes two to really change. You can't take credit for taking all the risks." She smiled down at him lovingly. "You really look terrible."

"I really—am beginning to—feel fine."

She shook her head. "You don't feel fine. You feel weak. And vulnerable."

"Do I?"

"Or you will," she said smoothly. Her fingers were busy for a moment, unbuttoning his shirt. She handled his belt like a pro and unhooked his slacks as though she'd had fairly recent practice. "Even now, you feel so weak," she said thoughtfully, "that I think you'd better just put your hands over your head where you won't be tempted to use them, Alan."

"Caro—"

"Look, I'm too busy for any more talking. I've got this hero in my life, you see. Or a man who's been thinking that he has to be a romantic hero . . . when he's been one, all along. Which leaves me with one terrific problem, I can tell you. Because your average, sensible, normal-type woman might not be enough for a hero. Luckily, Alan, *luckily* for you, I'm a very special woman. Or so someone has made me believe."

She stood up and reached behind her for the zipper at the back of her dress. In seconds, the gown shimmered to the floor. Beneath it, she was wearing a pale pink garter belt and stockings, matching a pink lace bra that laid no claims to practicality. Alan was responsible for such frivolous purchases, of course. She leaned over to tug off his slacks and shorts and socks.

"It could just be that I needed those roses, mind you," she said absently. "Maybe I *did* need to know I was more than a comfortable habit with you. Could it possibly be that you needed to know the same thing, though, love? That you weren't the only one who had to do a little changing?"

She popped the snap on her bra, slipped out of it. Her hands went to the garter belt and then paused. She just looked at him, mischief flashing in her eyes. And love, and wanting, and need. "Ever been made love to by a woman in a garter belt and stockings, Alan?"

His tongue was oddly thick, making speech difficult as he looked at her. "No."

"Good." She started at his toes, using the lash of her tongue, the tickle of her teeth, the pressure of her lips to seduce him. Really, it was past time she did a little wooing of her own. If she didn't know how, it was past time she learned.

When she finished with his toes, she moved up to his ankles, and shortly thereafter slid her length against him, rubbing her stocking-clad legs against his while she nipped and kissed circles on his chest.

She moved slowly, with infinite caution and care. Actually, she approached seducing him with a dogged, patient, methodical, and unquestionably feminine instinct. She wanted the man vulnerable. She wanted him to exult in feeling vulnerable; she wanted him free to express that vulnerability with her, to feel sure that there was nothing he need to hide from her ever again.

As a man, he'd made her feel the full scope of womanhood. As a woman, she had every intention of making him feel powerfully male . . . rich in manhood, the best of heroes, the sexiest of lovers.

And it was working. Without question, it was working. It wasn't just the increased tightening of his muscles that told her that, or the sheen of moisture rapidly coating his skin. It was in his eyes, those gentle blue eyes of his. So much love.

"You're failing to keep your hands under control," she remarked. "They're supposed to stay over your head."

"I can't help it. They won't."

She shrugged. If her hands wouldn't behave themselves, she could hardly blame his for being in the same mood. A woman in love had to be flexible.

So did a man. Alan was open to torture and was well aware his lady was having fun. But he'd never imagined that the rub of her stockings would send him over the edge of a deliciously high mountain. She wanted him out of control. That was exactly what she got. "I couldn't possibly love you more, Caro," he whispered, and coaxed her legs around him. The breath hushed from his lungs when he felt himself joined to her.

Both were suddenly, breathlessly anticipating the rhythm to come. That rhythm would happen, but the closeness for this moment was ecstasy, too. "I love you back," Carroll murmured softly, and then, "When are we getting married, Alan?"

"Yesterday."

"Not soon enough."

He was in perfect agreement with her on that.

SECOND CHANCE AT LOVE

COMING NEXT MONTH

TANGLING WITH WEBB #346 by Laine Allen
Writer's block drives whimsical Cristy McKnight
to a rash wager with wickedly handsome, infuriatingly
smug Webster Cannon: She'll concoct his
mystery if he'll pen her romance!

FRENCHMAN'S KISS #347 by Kerry Price
So what if he makes beautiful music, cooks
divinely, and kisses exquisitely? Thoroughly
unpredictable French composer Jean-Claude Delacroix
is *not* the reliable companion Sherry Seaton requires.

KID AT HEART #348 by Aimée Duvall
Where toy designer Lisa Fleming goes,
chaos follows—to the chagrin...and delight...
of toy company owner Chase Sanger, who begins
to hope he's found a lifelong playmate!

MY WILD IRISH ROGUE #349 by Helen Carter
Darkly handsome, joyfully spontaneous,
Liam Claire teases and tempts reserved Ingrid Peterson,
pursuing her across Ireland until she's nervous,
confused...and *very* aroused!

HAPPILY EVER AFTER #350 by Carole Buck
Lily Bancroft will do anything to get
the money—even dress as Snow White—but nothing
on earth will ever turn ruthlessly powerful
Dylan Chase into a fairy-tale prince.

TENDER TREASON #351 by Karen Keast
Wealthy, elusive, dictatorial Nyles Ryland electrifies
insurance investigator Lauren Kane with silken caresses
and drugging kisses. But she has no intention of playing
this week's lover to Grand Cayman's mystery man...

SECOND CHANCE AT LOVE

Be Sure to Read These New Releases!

SWANN'S SONG #334 by Carole Buck
Knowing both karate and kids, Megan Harper poses
as a nanny to secretly guard rock star Colin Swann and
his irrepressible son...and gets into deep
trouble when love complicates the deception!

STOLEN KISSES #335 by Liz Grady
Mattie Hamilton is rehearsing a museum
heist when tuxedo-clad thief Devlin Seamus Devlin
tackles her in midair...and offers to tutor
her in *all* kinds of midnight maneuvers!

GOLDEN GIRL #336 by Jacqueline Topaz
In sophisticated Hollywood, schoolteacher Olivia Gold
finds both her movie star grandmother *and* dashing soulmate
Andrew Carr—who transforms her into a glittering
golden girl and spellbinds her with sensual enchantment.

SMILES OF A SUMMER NIGHT #337 by Delaney Devers
Like a modern rogue, plantation owner
Jules Robichaux sweeps April Jasper away with cynical
charm, smoothly seduces her under moonlit
magnolias...but won't trust her enough to offer his love.

DESTINY'S DARLING #338 by Adrienne Edwards
"Bought" by ex-husband Bart Easton at a charity
benefit, Dot Biancardi recalls poignant moments—of
gallant courtship, wedded bliss...and lonely
heartache. Dare she risk repeating past mistakes?

WILD AND WONDERFUL #339 by Lee Williams
Trapped on a wild Maine island with brawny recluse
Greg Bowles, who's rejected the inheritance she's come to
give him, heir hunter Alicia Saunders finds a new
tension building...desire quickening.

Order on opposite page

SECOND CHANCE AT LOVE

Available at your local bookstore or return this form to:

SECOND CHANCE AT LOVE
THE BERKLEY PUBLISHING GROUP, Dept. B
390 Murray Hill Parkway, East Rutherford, NJ 07073

Please send me the titles checked above. I enclose _____. Include $1.00 for postage and handling if one book is ordered; 25¢ per book for two or more not to exceed $1.75. New York residents please add sales tax. Prices are subject to change without notice and may be higher in Canada.

NAME_____

ADDRESS_____

CITY_____ STATE/ZIP_____

(Allow six weeks for delivery.)   **SK-41b**

A STIRRING PAGEANTRY
OF
HISTORICAL ROMANCE

Shana Carrol

___ 0-515-08249-X Rebels in Love $3.95

Roberta Gellis

___ 0-515-07529-9 Fire Song $3.95
___ 0-515-08600-2 A Tapestry of Dreams $3.95

Jill Gregory

___ 0-515-07100-5 The Wayward Heart $3.50
___ 0-515-08710-6 My True and Tender Love $3.95
___ 0-515-08585-5 Moonlit Obsession $6.95
                   (A Jove Trade Paperback)

___ 0-515-08389-5 Promise Me The Dawn $3.95

Mary Pershall

___ 0-425-09171-6 A Shield of Roses $3.95
___ 0-425-09079-5 A Triumph of Roses $3.95

Francine Rivers

___ 0-515-08181-7 Sycamore Hill $3.50
___ 0-515-06823-3 This Golden Valley $3.50

Pamela Belle

___ 0-425-08268-7 The Moon in the Water $3.95
___ 0-425-07367-X The Chains of Fate $6.95
                   (A Berkley Trade Paperback)

Shannon Drake

___ 0-515-08637-1 Blue Heaven, Black Night $7.50
                   (A Jove Trade Paperback)

Available at your local bookstore or return this form to:

B **BERKLEY**
THE BERKLEY PUBLISHING GROUP, Dept. B
390 Murray Hill Parkway, East Rutherford, NJ 07073

Please send me the titles checked above. I enclose _____. Include $1.00 for postage
and handling if one book is ordered; 25¢ per book for two or more not to exceed $1.75.
California, Illinois, New Jersey and Tennessee residents please add sales tax. Prices
subject to change without notice and may be higher in Canada.

NAME_____

ADDRESS_____

CITY_____STATE/ZIP_____

(Allow six weeks for delivery.)

435